Integrating the Literature of Maurice Sendak in the Classroom

by
Thomas J. Palumbo

illustrated by Vanessa Filkins

Cover by Vanessa Filkins

Copyright © 1993, Good Apple

Good Apple
1204 Buchanan St., Box 299
Carthage, IL 62321-0299

SIMON & SCHUSTER *A Paramount Communications Company*

Good Apple
1204 Buchanan St., Box 299
Carthage, IL 62321-0299

Table of Contents

iii   GA1430

Introducing Maurice Sendak

What Makes a Successful Author and Illustrator?

Integrating the Literature of Maurice Sendak in the Classroom is the fourth book in a five-part series focusing on the most read contemporary authors and illustrators. Like the books before it, *Integrating the Literature of Judy Blume in the Classroom*, *Integrating the Literature of Beverly Cleary in the Classroom* and *Integrating the Literature of Chris Van Allsburg in the Classroom*, this book uses the eleven-step format necessary for developing and maximizing the educational benefits of literature used in the classroom or home. Each of the steps is multilevel and can be read to or read with or by children when doing each activity. The activities are not etched in stone. They are springboards to further study and to the works of other authors and illustrators. You do not have to do all the questions and investigations. Use the ideas that fit your educational goals and objectives, as well as the learning styles of your students. After you blend the four books from this series with your reading, literature and language arts curricula, combine your ideas and teaching style with each selection. You will then find that there are very few gaps in your classroom and school program.

About the Author

For the past twenty-five years Maurice Sendak's stories, illustrations, essays and critical reviews have provided pages of thought-provoking ideas to the teaching and reading community. He has taken us from the island of the wild things to the home of Pierre to the Mother Goose Theater. Through the uniqueness and quality of his illustrations, he has demonstrated the importance of artwork in children's books and paved the way for a renaissance of children's book illustrators. Through the creativity of his stories, he has given multiskilled children needed direction for their writing and drawing skills. For teachers, he has shown us that illustrations do have a musical quality, and by understanding this we are better able to understand the liveliness that illustrations for children should convey. Sendak calls this "the essence of the picture book."

Maurice Sendak's *Caldecott & Company...Notes on Books and Authors* is a must for anyone using Maurice Sendak as part of his classroom program.

Maurice Sendak was born on June 10, 1928. The place was Brooklyn, New York. He knew at the age of five that he wanted to be an author and an illustrator. His father was a gifted storyteller who weaved magic ideas in stories without the help of a book. The first book that Maurice Sendak illustrated was Marcel Ayme's *Wonderful Farm*. Ruth Krause inspired his earlier works and gave direction to many of his ideas. *Kenny's Window* was the first book that he wrote and illustrated. Maurice Sendak is Philadelphia's adopted son in the area of children's books and their illustrations. His illustrations in *Where the Wild Things Are* caused a national revival, started a revolution, gave new impetus into the importance of illustrated children's books. It is only natural, then, that one of the books in this five-part literature series focuses on his stories and illustrations. The Rosenbach Museum at Twenty-Second and Delancy Place in Philadelphia, Pennsylvania, has a room filled with every book that Sendak wrote or illustrated. Not including his play version of the *Nutcracker* and *Where the Wild Things Are*, his creative count is past ninety. Even though this museum is a converted row house, thousands of area children visit the Sendak display room every year.

GA1430

Questions You Might Want to Ask Before Using This Guide

Before doing the activities in this book or visiting the museum if you are in the area, answering the following questions will give you a head start in appreciating the works of this outstanding illustrator and storyteller.

1. Children's books had been illustrated for hundreds of years before Maurice Sendak came along. Why, then, is he recognized as being so important in opening the gates of recognition for present day illustrators and their illustrations?_____
_____
_____

2. Where are Maurice Sendak's books displayed in the Rosenbach Museum? Tell us the room and the exact location of these works. Note: The author realizes that this is not an easy task. I feel that you will really enjoy the answer to this question. Some good research on your part will lead to this problem's solutions. _____
_____
_____

3. What illustrators influenced Maurice Sendak's drawings? _____
_____

4. Maurice Sendak talks about seeing musical qualities in good artwork. What could possibly remind him of music in the paintings he draws or appreciates?_____
_____
_____

5. What do you expect to learn from using this resource book?_____
_____
_____

6. If you were asked to write a book about a famous author, who would you choose for your selection? Why?_____
_____
_____
_____

7. How do you select a book you are going to read? Do you enjoy books that imitate real life or books that bring out feelings like happiness, sadness and loneliness? Ask your teacher why he/she chose this book and record his/her answer on the back of this paper, also._____
_____
_____
_____
_____

GA1430

8. Examine the artwork in three of Maurice Sendak's illustrated books. Can you find the works of three women illustrators that are close to Maurice Sendak's style? Please record the female illustrators' names and the book(s) that you feel are similar to Sendak's.

a. _____ _____

b. _____ _____

c. _____ _____

9. Have you read any of Maurice Sendak's books? If you have, which book do you think could be made into a cartoon series? Why? _____

_____

10. If you haven't read any of Maurice Sendak's books, what book have you read lately that could be made into a television or cartoon series? Please explain why your idea for a show should be considered over the book ideas of your classmates. _____

_____

11. Imagine that you are the curator of the Rosenbach Museum. A group of librarians and teachers of children's literature are entering your museum. How would you begin to address this group about your Sendak display? Please remember that there are many other things in this museum that this group may be interested in investigating. _____

_____

_____

12. As this same curator, your board of directors has asked you to plan three more illustrator displays. You are to focus on the contributions of minorities in the field of book art. What female, African American, Hispanic, Native American Indian or Oriental illustrators would you feature? Be sure to mention their best works in your presentation to your directors. ____

_____

_____

13. How would you encourage children and adults of all ages to read a Maurice Sendak book or buy an illustrated poster of one of his book illustrations? _____

_____

_____

Outside Over There

Eggshell Sitting Family Protector Musical Horn

Baby-Sitter's Fault A Sea Song Saved Sister

Goblin Mischief Tumbling Ida

Lead-Ins to Literature

One second Ida is standing at the window playing a musical instrument. The very next second she is chasing goblins in a world called Outside Over There. The goblins kidnapped her baby sister to participate in a special ceremony. An old rhyme and a bit of wisdom help her on her quest but not before some strange happenings almost destroy Ida and her sister. Do you feel that young girls, without any help, should chase after goblins? After reading the selection even the bravest warrior might not ever take off after a goblin again.

1. What are the first three things that come to mind when someone mentions that goblins are involved in the story? _____

_____

_____

_____

2. If you designed a goblin for a story, what four special powers would you give it? How would its powers differ if you made it a male or a female? _____

_____

_____

_____

_____

3. When the baby was stolen, the goblins left something in its place so Ida wouldn't notice that the baby was missing. What two things would you have left to fool Ida?_____

_____

4. Outside Over There is a strange name for a place. What other stories have you read that talked about mysterious places? List five places that you and a friend can recall from children's books. _____

_____

_____

5. What are three things that you might advise Ida to do before starting out to capture her sister back from the goblins? _____

_____

6. Would you accept a stranger's offer to help her find the goblins who stole her sister? Discuss three reasons why you would go and three why you wouldn't go. See if you can make a humorous reason in each category, also. (I can't go, Ida, because my shoes are at the shoemakers being repaired, and you know you can't walk on thorny goblin ground without a good pair of shoes. _____

_____

_____

7. What are the first three things you would have said when you found your sister missing from her crib? What would your mother have said upon finding the baby missing? _____

_____

_____

Just the Facts

1. Is this a modern story or a story from olden times? How could you tell? _____

   _____

2. Where did Papa go? _____

3. What is an arbor? _____

4. What musical instrument did Ida play? _____

5. How many goblins were needed to steal Ida's sister away through the window? _____

6. Why did they steal her sister? _____

7. What was the changeling? _____

8. What two things did the ice baby do? _____

9. What garment did Ida take with her on her mission to recover her baby sister? _____

   _____

10. How should Ida have left the house? _____

11. Where did the goblins hide the baby? _____

12. To gain power, Ida had to turn around in the _____.

13. What was ringed-round in the story? _____

14. How did Ida's father get word to Ida and her mother? _____

15. Where did Ida find her sister sitting cozily? _____

16. What did the goblins change into when Ida played her horn? _____

17. What type of dance did the goblins do? _____

18. Ida landed in the middle of a _____.

19. What were the goblins disguised as? _____

20. What word described the goblin wedding? _____

3

GA1430

⁇⁈⁉ **What Is Your Opinion?** ⁇⁈⁉

1. What age do you think children should be before they are left home baby-sitting for their younger brothers and sisters? _____

2. Who do you think are better baby-sitters, boys or girls? Why?_____
_____

3. Do you think it was really Ida's fault that the baby was taken when she was looking out the window?_____
_____

4. If you were writing a story about a missing baby in a house, where are the first three places that you would look for the baby? _____
_____
_____

5. Many older children think baby-sitting is the worst job that they can be given. What do you think are the five worst jobs that children are asked to do? Please describe your five choices and place baby-sitting in its correct rank order?
_____
_____
_____
_____
_____
_____

6. Goblins are always given a bad rap in children's stories. What three attributes could you give to goblins in a story that would make them more enjoyable and less frightening?
_____
_____
_____

7. How would you rate Maurice Sendak's illustrations in *Outside Over There* compared to the more honored illustrations in *Where the Wild Things Are?* What criteria should children use in evaluating the illustrations in books they read? _____
_____
_____

8. What could the goblins have done or left to make their kidnapping not known for a longer period of time? _____
_____

9. Would you have enjoyed this story more or less if it were completely in rhyme form? Why? _____
_____
_____

10. What is the best and worst baby-sitting story you've ever heard? Use the back of this paper for your selections.

Vexing Vocabulary

One of the hardest jobs a teacher has is teaching students to make their own decisions on what is important to study. Instead of studying things you already know, this work sheet will give you a chance to generate words that you don't know. Words that you think are special or words that you would like to remember should also be recorded below.

What two words would you pick from *Outside Over There* to study in each of the following categories:

1. a baby's actions _____ _____

2. monsters _____ _____

3. big sister _____ _____

4. secrets _____ _____

5. a compound word _____ _____

6. an adjective _____ _____

7. an interesting sentence _____

8. a well-written phrase _____

_____

9. the hardest spelling word _____ _____

10. a homograph _____ _____

Select ten words from the story that would add to your writing skills. Record them on the blanks below. You are writing a goblin song. Use the ten words below in your song.

_____ _____ _____ _____ _____

_____ _____ _____ _____ _____

Song title: _____ Song's subject: _____

_____

_____

_____

_____

_____

_____

What is important to study?

GA1430

We Are Small but We Are Tough
Drills for Skills (Genius Level)

Most people get excited about learning large and fancy words. They sometimes forget that small words can be just as tough as their longer friends. Each answer below is a four-letter word. To make the activity difficult, each four-letter answer must contain three vowels and one consonant. For this activity *Y* and *W* are not vowels. If you like, you can then take the ultimate challenge. This can be performed by adding a letter of your own to the four given, rearranging the letters and making a five-letter word.

Clue	Answer	Ultimate Challenge
Example: the roof's edge	eave	weave
1. a type of cookie		
2. a rug measure		
3. butter substitute		
4. glow around a body		
5. on the ocean		
6. opera song		
7. first _____ (help)		
8. a continent		
9. French boyfriend		
10. a fencing sword		
11. moisturizer plant		
12. a great lake		
13. to drip slowly		
14. completed with		
15. away from wind		
16. in place of		
17. a smart thought		

Can you think of any words we might have missed in this search for four-letter words with three vowels? List them below.

GA1430

Which Witch Bewitches You?
Short-Term Project

Teacher Note: Encyclopedias are filled with articles on myths and witchcraft. Many religions forbid their children to research such topics, so please check with parents and students before starting this "witch hunt."

There is an endless array of myth and witch topics. This sheet is designed for you to get a taste of many different topics. Place one comment next to each topic on the left. Then, on your own, try to find out some additional facts to make yourself more knowledgeable in the areas discussed.

Topics   **Intelligent but Brief Comment**

1. Circe_____

_____

2. Bible reference (Exodus 22:18) _____

_____

3. The ogre in "The Three Billy Goats Gruff"_____

_____

4. Wicked Witch of the West in the *Wizard of Oz* _____

_____

5. 1692 Massachusetts witch hunt _____

_____

6. Medusa_____

_____

7. The sirens _____

_____

8. The Lorelei _____

_____

9. The troll_____

_____

10. The ghosts of Christmas past, present and future _____

_____

11. The muses _____

_____

12. Jack's giant _____

_____

GA1430

Good Goblins vs. Evil Goblins
Ideas and Illustrations

Why were imaginary monsters originally created? What went through a writer's or illustrator's mind when he/she (remember, Mary Shelley, a woman, created Frankenstein) designed the first witch, ghoul, cyclops, ogre, phantom or goblin for his/her story? Were these new creatures originally meant to be helpful characters, or were they always meant to scare, frighten and do unspeakable deeds? How do you think children would grow up if monsters were never created and children never had anything to be frightened about?

The four boxes below are designed to accommodate your goblin illustrations. The first box has an evil set of eyes that you are to build a face around, the second a facial outline, the third a hairy body, the fourth a geometric shape for a goblin that came out of a computer in the year 2000. Complete each picture. Enlarge your best picture of the four to put up on a classroom clothesline.

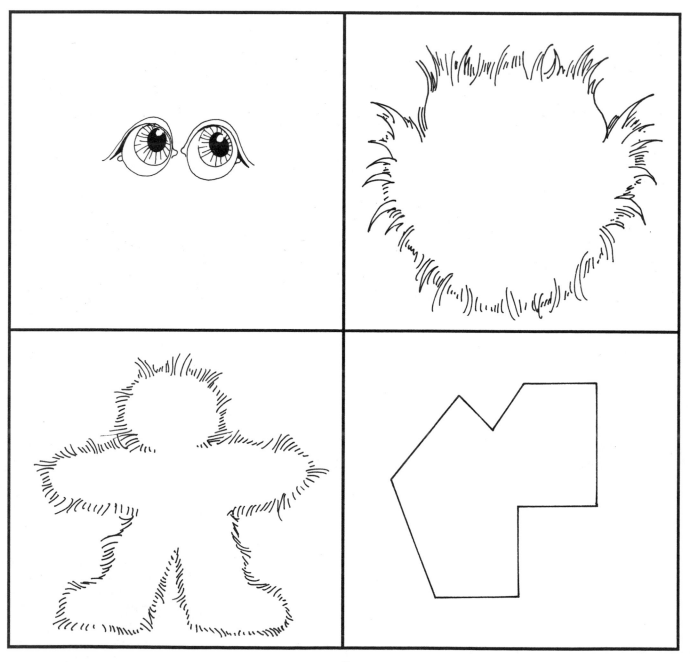

8

GA1430

Student Suggestions

1. Review the song "Teddy Bears Picnic." Using the same musical scheme, write the song about a goblin picnic. See if you can mention Ida and her sister in your writing. If this song doesn't appeal to you, choose one you feel more comfortable in changing.

2. See if you can find the origin of the word *goblin*. When was it first used and who was the originator of the word?

3. After studying the art of making flow charts with your teacher, make a flow chart describing the story. List Ida's options each time she had a choice to make. Out the window, forward or backward would be the two branches to the flow chart that should then be drawn.

4. The ice business has certainly changed from years ago. Focus on the changes in the last few years. Why is it a very profitable business?

5. Invite an ice sculptor to give a demonstration to your class. Tell your students to watch closely because the treat won't last long!

6. Research the last whaling ship now docked in Mystic, Connecticut. Write the Chamber of Commerce or Connecticut Tourist Information Bureau for information.

7. What is scrimshaw? Research the topic and have a scrimshaw creating contest in your classroom.

8. Visit a maritime museum. If you live in the desert, write to a maritime museum for information.

9. Pick three jobs that Ida's father might have on a ship. Write three diary entries, one for each job, describing the job and how much he misses the family.

10. Make a catalog of antique and present day cribs.

11. Baby dressing gowns were very fashionable during the time of this story. Design three patterns that you might find on a baby's dressing gown.

12. Imagine you are the minister of a goblin wedding. Write the words that you and the wedding party might say.

13. Make a travel poster for three places a goblin might go on his wedding.

14. Write a new part for a character that will help Ida find her sister.

9

GA1430

Teacher Suggestions

1. Have your class predict the ten favorite outdoor and indoor activities of children in another class in your school. Each child in your class then picks a partner from another class who fills out a blank list asking for his ten favorite indoor and outdoor activities. Each student scores one point for each answer that matches one of his predictions. Hundreds of other prediction topics could also be used in this format.

2. Design a short-term project called "Ida Meets the Corn People." Each child takes an ear of corn and transforms it into a member of the Corn People Society. Encourage good characteristics of these people from your students, instead of making them baby snatchers. Most classrooms have each child adopt an egg and tell its life story. Ears of corn have generated far more creative and humorous ideas. Each child dresses, names and presents his corn person and creates/presents that corn person's average day.

3. Create a baby-sitter school and have your class select and describe the classes that a baby-sitter would have to take.

4. Show your class some of the newest baby protection devices, from the Walkie Talkie-like listening devices to the normal car seat. Then encourage them to design and illustrate some of their own.

5. Research with your class the most common home accidents that involve children. Divide into groups and have your class brainstorm, then present to their classmates ways of avoiding these problems.

6. Have each student design a video game or board game called Outside Over There.

7. Have each child in your class walk one block backward and record what he sees. Discuss what would be the creative aspects and pitfalls of having a world in which everyone walks backwards. One of my students said school would have to start an hour later because he could never get to school on time walking backwards.

8. Discuss how Ida might have rigged a baby alarm or some type of anti-goblin device in her home.

9. Have your class design a page (words and illustrations) that could be added to the story *Outside Over There*. This could be followed with a discussion topic . . . If you could enter the story for one minute, where would you enter the story and what would you do?

10. Have your class make Good and Bad charts showing the good and bad aspects of having the ability to fly. (bad) It would put a lot of people out of business. (good) Air pollution would be eliminated.

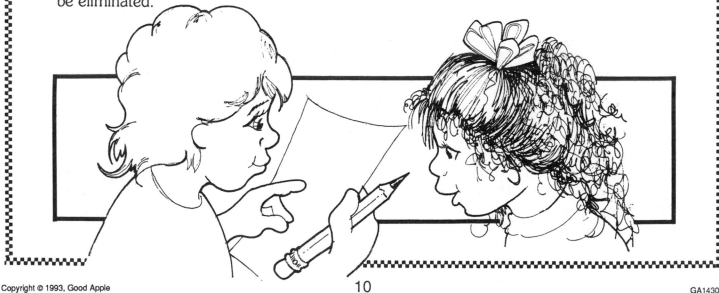

10

GA1430

Write Like a Master

The theme for the story starters below centers on an older brother or sister that doesn't want to, once again, get stuck with watching the baby on a weekend night. Try to put yourself into that person's shoes. Write the way he/she would act, not the way you would act.

Story Starter I

I know the baby is around here somewhere. How far could she crawl in the "one minute" that I was on the phone talking to Beth? "Here, Melissa sweetie. It is your _____ (pet name for yourself) calling." Where can she_____

_____

_____

_____

Story Starter II

Mom, it isn't fair. This is three weeks in a row that I have had to watch "Old Wet Diapers" himself. I should be outside with my friends learning about life and playing. You always_____

_____

_____

_____

Story Starter III

I think the baby ate the dog's puppy chow. He keeps barking and rolling over. Not the dog! The baby! No, I am not goofy. I have heard of cases where babies ate _____ (name an item or food) and became _____

_____

_____

_____

Story Starter IV

This is the best baby product that I have ever created! If you think my baby alarm was great, wait until you see _____

_____

_____

_____

Story Starter V

How about this same situation from the baby's eyes? I know the baby can't talk, but imagine what it would be thinking.

Look at this goof trying to get my diaper on. He is doing it backwards. Who is this Goo, Goo he keeps talking about? Can't this dummy speak English? Maybe I should _____

_____

_____

11

GA1430

Gameboard

Materials Needed: Two number cubes, movers, light-colored crayons; Vexing Vocabulary; Just the Facts. Student-made and teacher-made question cards can be placed in the areas provided for them on the gameboard. They are optional but highly recommended. A card is picked each time a player has a multiple of five points in his/her bank (5, 10, 15, 20 or 25).

Players Needed: Two to four players or teams of two players

Play Procedures: Players alternate turns; throw number cubes; move in either direction at any time. This allows for playing strategies, rather than just mindlessly moving around a gameboard.

The Roll: Roll both number cubes. Your teacher will tell you to conduct some math operations with the number cubes. The three rules used most often in my classroom are

(a) Subtract the smaller from the larger; then move that many spaces (6 - 4 = 2). Move two spaces.

(b) Multiply the two cubes and move the number of spaces in the one's column of the answer (2 x 6 = 12). Move two spaces.

(c) Keep on adding the two cubes until you get one digit as the answer (6 + 6 = 12, 12 = 1 + 2 = 3). Move three spaces. Mathematicians call this finding the digital root.

Object: To score twenty-five points or to capture four creatures, baby-sitters, family members or babies. Owning creatures, baby-sitters, family members or babies can be accomplished by landing on them in a normal turn, trading for them when you land on a trading post or buying one of them for two times their value when you land on the bank. Each time you land on a property, you color in (or initial) the little block in the corner of the property and put the points in your running bank. Ownership will change after trades only. Cross them out on the score sheet and add them to the other column. A scoreboard is provided for you. Each time someone lands on your property, he must pay you the number of points indicated in the top right-hand corner. Each time you land on your own property, you receive twice the points shown.

Winning Sets: Creatures (goblin, gremlin, nymph and ghoul); baby-sitters (sleeping, crying, fed up and frazzled); family members (mom, dad, sis and dog); babies (walking, talking, crawling and eating)

Player One's Properties/Score	Player Two's Properties/Score

GA1430

Game Card Property Pieces

On this page are the sixteen game pieces for *Outside Over There*. Cut them out and place them on oaktag to prolong their usability. Place a little box next to the gameboard as a storage area. Each time someone lands on an appropriate board space, he receives points and one of the game cards to verify property ownership. It also makes property trading much easier. The next time you play the game, design your own game card property pieces. Design a gameboard and create your own educational board game. Pick a theme. Then try to add important facts and intellectual flavor to your game.

13

Outside Over There

START | 1
PICK A FACT CARD | 2 | 3 | 4 | 5 | 6

Fact Cards

BANK BANK | 23
BANK BANK | 24
7 | 8

TRADING POST | 16 | 17 | 18 | 19 | 20 | 21 | 22
23 | 24
25 | 26 | PICK A VOCABULARY CARD | 27 | 28 | 29 | FINISH | 30

9 | 10
PICK A TOSS-UP | 11 | 12 | 13 | 14
TRADING POST | 15

Toss Up Cards

Vocabulary Cards

14

In the Night Kitchen

Mickey Batter

Bakers

Chanting

Noises

Night

What's Cooking?   Milky Way

Cake-Free Bed Kitchen Surprises Dough Plane

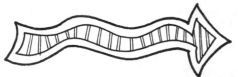
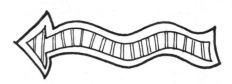

Lead-Ins to Literature

One minute you are snug in your bed, and the next minute you are flying into the air over sleeping family members and tall buildings. Your flight stops at the night kitchen where everything that is found on the morning breakfast table is being made. All of a sudden you become part of the batter of bread that is going to be eaten the next morning. You are trying to escape and then. . . .

1. What is the funniest thing that ever happened to you in the kitchen of your house? _____

_____

2. If you were writing a story about strange bakers who bake in the night, what would you make them look like? Would you make them scary or make them just like ordinary everyday bakers?

_____

_____

3. Witches in stories like this are always making some kind of brew or potion. What three things appear/are cooked most often in the children's stories that you have read? _____

_____

4. Pick five parts of a home (kitchen, attic, basement, underground tunnel, beneath the porch, etc.) and rate them for "scariness" in children's stories. Which location of a house would you pick for a night story? What events do you have planned for the room you picked? _____

_____

5. Many people find themselves flying in their dreams. Why do you think flying appeals to so many people? Why do most of our comic book heroes and heroines have the ability to fly? Do you think our skies would be too crowded if everyone could fly? _____

_____

6. What do you think is the favorite cookie, cake and pie of your classmates? _____

_____

7. When you read a scary story or see a scary movie, which do you think is scarier, strange noises or silence? Why? _____

_____

8. Old-time bakers always wore white and a big baker's cap. How would you describe or dress the modern baker? _____

_____

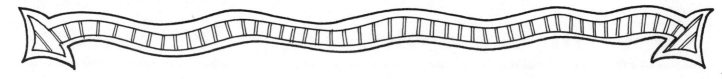

GA1430

★ ★ ★ ★ ★ Just the Facts ★ ★ ★ ★ ★

1. Can you name three of the five sounds that Mickey heard when trying to fall asleep? _____

_____

2. In what year was *In the Night Kitchen* written and for whom was it written? _____

_____

3. What did Mickey lose when he fell through the dark? _____

4. What were the first three things that Mickey flew past in the beginning of his travels?

_____

5. What time do the bakers bake till? _____

6. The bakers were patterned after what two famous comedians? _____

7. The bakers thought that they were putting a delicious _____ in the oven.

8. What part of the cake did the bakers think Mickey was? _____

9. What did Mickey make out of bread dough? Why? _____

10. Why did Mickey grab the cup from the bakers? _____

11. Can you name the group of stars that Mickey flew over on his way to get the baker's milk?

_____

12. Where did Mickey's swimming skills help him? _____

13. What delivered Mickey back into his bed? _____

Write three facts about the story or its illustrations.

1. _____

2. _____

3. _____

GA1430

What Is Your Opinion?

1. How old do you think Mickey is? Why? _____

   _____

2. In some of the drawings in this story Mickey looks like an older child; in other drawings he looks like a baby. Why do you think the author drew him in two different ways? _____

   _____

   _____

3. Do you think this story was meant to be scary, funny or both? What parts, in your opinion, might be considered scary or funny? _____

   _____

4. The story had only Mickey and the bakers in it. What additional characters would you have added to the story to make it more interesting? _____

   _____

5. What illustration did you like best? How would you change the cover illustration if you wanted the story to be scarier? _____

   _____

6. What would you guess are the three favorite types of breads liked by your classmates? Can you pick the three exotic types of bread that would also be in a top three in your classmates' choices? Where do you think bagels or cinnamon buns would fall on your classmates' lists?

   _____

   _____

7. The dough plane is a creative idea within the story theme. What other creative ideas might you point out if you were reading this story to a group of young children? _____

   _____

8. Most families do not have morning cake for breakfast. Would the story be just as interesting if the child was transported to a cereal, toast or muffin factory? What breakfast product would you have featured in the story? _____

   _____

9. What three things would you add to this story to attract older or younger readers?

   _____

   _____

Vexing Vocabulary

middle	measuring	oven
poked	through	scrape
below	fuss	batter
every	pouring	flew
kneaded	pounded	yawn
quiet	racket	slid
chanting	shouted	heard
delicious	stir	clothes

Everything that you could possibly think of doing with a vocabulary word will be included on this page. Rhyme the vocabulary word with a similar ending, rhyme it with an unlike ending word, record a synonym, record an antonym and where possible list its homonym. Score one point for each task you complete, and total your score to the right of each line. Compare your score on the whole page with someone in your class that you would like to compete against. Some can't be completed and some have more than one good solution.

Word	Like Ending	Unlike Ending	Synonym	Antonym	Homonym	Total
flew	blew	true	soared	crawled	flu	
stir						
oven						
heard						
through						
middle						
below						
kneaded						
scrape						
yawn						
clothes						

Pick four words of your own. Complete all five operations.

Word	Like Ending	Unlike Ending	Synonym	Antonym	Homonym	Total
1.						
2.						
3.						
4.						

Drills for Skills

There are many things that are common in kitchens across the country or even in your neighborhood. There are also many things that only few kitchens have. You are being sent on a word safari hunt through your kitchen. To make it harder you are to find things that begin with the letters *K I T C H E N*. For each letter you are to locate five words. Place an *M* next to the word that you think is most common. Place an *L* next to the least common word. This word should be one that few people would include on their lists. Draw a small picture of one of the five items that you used for each letter.

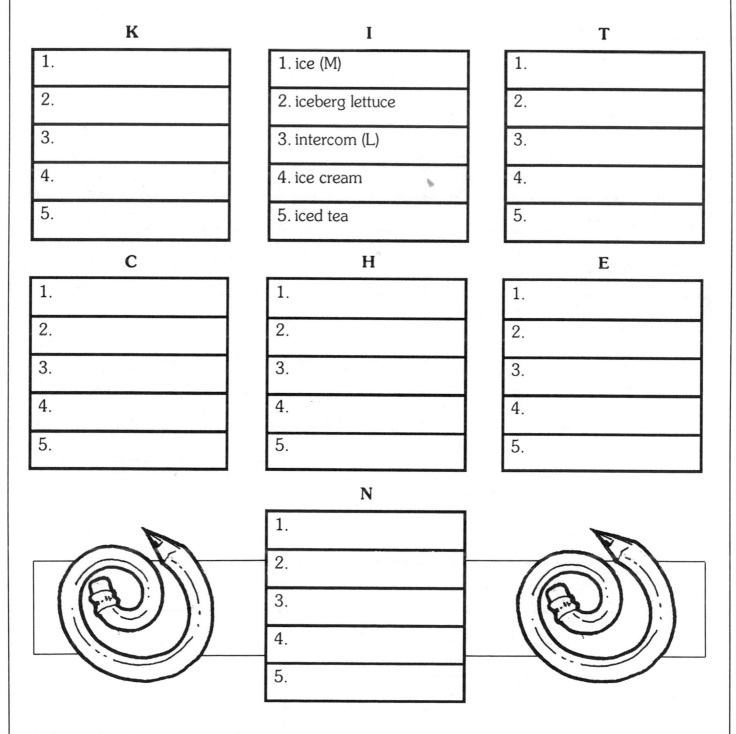

K

1.
2.
3.
4.
5.

I

1. ice (M)
2. iceberg lettuce
3. intercom (L)
4. ice cream
5. iced tea

T

1.
2.
3.
4.
5.

C

1.
2.
3.
4.
5.

H

1.
2.
3.
4.
5.

E

1.
2.
3.
4.
5.

N

1.
2.
3.
4.
5.

Pick another kitchen word of your own (toaster, oven, microwave) and see if you can form a more challenging list.

Ideas and Illustrations

Below you will find the wrapping surrounding four loaves of bread. Research the styles/designs of bread wrap at your local supermarket or convenience store. Then copy the two designs that you picked as the most *eye-catching* or *best-drawn*. On the remaining two draw your own designs for a loaf of bread that is being made with your family name on it.

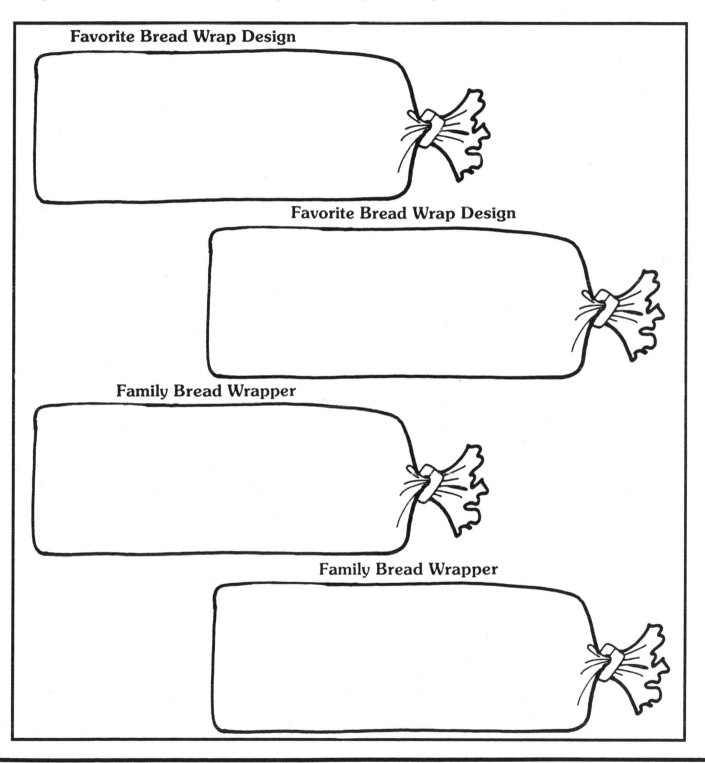

Favorite Bread Wrap Design

Favorite Bread Wrap Design

Family Bread Wrapper

Family Bread Wrapper

Draw four milk cartons on the back of this paper and design a milk logo that would represent your family milk company.

GA1430

Short-Term Project

Your parents probably watched an old-time comedian named Jackie Gleason. He had a comedy show that almost completely took place in his kitchen each week. You are a writer for six different shows, and you are being asked to write a kitchen scene for each one. Use six pieces of paper and place them in a booklet form for each of your ideas. Use the space below to outline your ideas. Create the scene for each story and draw an illustration to go with it. If you are not a great artist, ask a classmate to draw a few of the important props.

Bugs Bunny's Kitchen Story	Dracula's Kitchen Story	Snow White's Kitchen Story
Elvis Presley's Kitchen Story	My Mom's Kitchen Story	Wicked Witch's Kitchen Story

If you have a better choice for a kitchen scene, change the one's given after clearing your ideas with a teacher. Maybe your teacher will allow you to pick a different room of the house for your six scenes.

Student Suggestions

1. Design a survey for your classmates on what eating utensil they think is the most important.

2. Research the origin of the knife, spoon and fork and how they were used by different cultures. Did you know that the fork was the last one to be created?

3. Imagine that you have a television show titled _____ (your name) *Place*. Create a one-minute announcement about your show or a one-minute demonstration of your kitchen ideas.

4. Get a sink, fixture or cabinet catalog and use the cutout pictures to design the ideal kitchen.

5. Take a survey of your classmates of the three night jobs they would like to have if they decided to work nights. How many night jobs would involve work outside, in a factory, home or office?

6. Research the process of making bread.

7. Write to Nabisco and some of the other major cookie companies for a list of their top ten products and compare them with lists your classmates have prepared.

8. Ask a local pizza maker or bread man to do a classroom demonstration on the art of making pizza and bread.

9. Pick a kitchen appliance (stove, oven, refrigerator, freezer, toaster, microwave, popcorn machine, etc.) and trace its origin and development.

10. Write a sales buying pitch for a 1930 stove and one for a modern stove. If you do not like the stove, then make believe you are a car salesman of forty years ago selling a 1950 Ford; then sell a 1992 Ford. Divide a piece of paper into two columns. Place a 1950 and 1992 car at the top. Complete an ad, highlighting the special features of each. Other choices might include a camera, motorcycle, mobile home, juice maker, television or razor.

11. Write a mini report on the pros and cons of day and night baseball. Which one of the two choices do you think your classmates think is better for the players? The fans? The neighborhoods the ballparks are in? The local economy? Television coverage? Advertisers?

12. Write a tall tale about an event that took place in your kitchen.

GA1430

Teacher Suggestions

1. Discuss with your class what a night shift involves in the terms of work, coordination of family schedules, and worker productivity. Make a bulletin board with your students highlighting the pluses and minuses of working a night job.

2. Have a Night Shift Dress Up Day where students give mini presentations on the importance of the night jobs that they perform.

3. Research the types of music that someone on a night shift might listen to while working. Design a class questionnaire on "Would music improve someone's work and productivity, or would it take away from his concentration on the night shift?"

4. Many supermarkets are now open twenty-four hours, so people on the night shift who sleep in the day can shop. What other types of businesses do your students think might survive at night or would night shift workers like opened?

5. Research the labels of famous manufacturers in the food and other industries. What is the benefit of a recognizable label?

6. The *Guinness Book of World Records* has many records pertaining to food. Have your students highlight their five favorites.

7. Create a night shift television show with your class with in-depth interviews and reports on night shift happenings. Highlight features called "The Loneliest Night Shift Job" and "Night Shift Humor."

8. Have each of your students make a night shift acrostic poem by writing *night shift* downward and putting in a night occupation and illustration for each letter.

9. Have your class develop posters called "History That Happened at Night." What historical events happened at night?

10. You awake in the middle of the night and head for the kitchen. Name five of the most frequent things people would do at this time; then pick five less-thought-of ideas.

11. Have your class research songs that have *night* in the title or involve things that happen in the night. The song "Nightshift" could be played and discussed.

12. Listen to the song "9 to 5" and see if your class can come up with lyrics for a song entitled "12 to 7."

24

GA1430

Oral Storytelling
Write Like a Master

The theme for the story starters below is the mysterious batter or dough that you are whipping up in the kitchen. Please continue each theme by writing your ideas in the spaces below or continuing the story theme in a talk in front of your classmates.

Story Starter/Oral Theme I
This chocolate chip cookie dough isn't like the other batches we made this week. I put the same amount of milk, flour, eggs and chips in it, but from the time I first put my hands in the mix, it felt strange. I looked at my hands. The cut on my finger wasn't there any more. The freckles on the back of my wrist weren't there, either. My_____

_____

_____

_____

Story Starter/Oral Theme II
My hands are stuck in the batter. I can't pull them out. The batter seems to be turning into concrete. The bowl is so heavy that I can't even move it off the table to try to crack it. My sister tried to pull me out and now she is stuck fast, also. This can't be the golden goose story with a bowl of batter. No one _____

_____

_____

_____

Story Starter/Oral Theme III
The cookie dough is moving by itself. I am not talking about just rising. I am talking about walking across the kitchen counter. I hit it with a spatula, and it seemed to give off a laughing sound. It walked right over _____

_____

_____

_____

Story Starter/Oral Theme IV
Can Oreo cookies make you smarter? I never ate the outside of an Oreo. I'd just break them open and lick the cream. Mom would find outsides of cookies all over the house. She caught me in the middle of a lick one day and forced me to eat the whole cookie. My mind seemed to tingle. From that time on _____

_____

_____

_____

GA1430

Gameboard

Materials Needed: Two number cubes, movers, light-colored crayons; Vexing Vocabulary; Just the Facts. Student-made and teacher-made question cards can be placed in the areas provided for them on the gameboard. They are optional but highly recommended. A card is picked each time a player has a multiple of five points in his/her bank (5, 10, 15, 20 or 25).

Players Needed: Two to four players or teams of two players

Play Procedures: Players alternate turns; throw number cubes; move in either direction at any time. This allows for playing strategies, rather than just mindlessly moving around a gameboard.

The Roll: Roll both number cubes. Your teacher will tell you to conduct some math operations with the number cubes. The three rules used most often in my classroom are

(a) Subtract the smaller from the larger; then move that many spaces (6 - 4 = 2). Move two spaces.

(b) Multiply the two cubes and move the number of spaces in the one's column of the answer (2 x 6 = 12). Move two spaces.

(c) Keep on adding the two cubes until you get one digit as the answer (6 + 6 = 12, 12 = 1 + 2 = 3). Move three spaces. Mathematicians call this finding the digital root.

Object: To score twenty-five points or to capture four breakfast foods, breads, drinks or solar bodies. Owning breakfast foods, breads, drinks or solar bodies can be accomplished by landing on them in a normal turn, trading for them when you land on a trading post or buying one of them for two times their value when you land on the bank. Each time you land on a property, you color in (or initial) the little block in the corner of the property and put the points in your running bank. Ownership will change after trades only. Cross them out on the score sheet and add them to the other column. A scoreboard is provided for you. Each time someone lands on your property, he must pay you the number of points indicated in the top right-hand corner. Each time you land on your own property, you receive twice the points shown.

Winning Sets: Breakfast foods (pancakes, eggs, bacon and cereal); breads (rye, whole wheat, Italian and garlic); drinks (orange juice, apple juice, white milk and chocolate milk); solar bodies (sun, moon, stars and planets)

Player One's Properties/Score	Player Two's Properties/Score

Game Card Property Pieces

On this page are the sixteen pieces for *In the Night Kitchen*. Cut them out and place them on oaktag to prolong their usability. Place a little box next to the gameboard as a storage area. Each time someone lands on an appropriate board space, he receives points and one of the game cards to verify property ownership. It also makes property trading much easier. The next time you play the game, design your own game card property pieces. Design a gameboard and create your own educational board game. Pick a theme. Then try to add important facts and intellectual flavor to your game.

GA1430

In the Night Kitchen

GA1430

Where the Wild Things Are

Max's Voyage   King Max

Looking for Mischief

Wild Thing Dance

Gnashing Teeth

Supperless Boy

Bedroom Forest   Magic Stare

GA1430

Lead-Ins to Literature

Did you ever wonder where the wild monsters in your stories and dreams go when they are not scaring people? Do you think that the monster in your favorite children's story is terrible when he goes home to meet his parents? Do you think that monsters are just putting on an act and pretending when they are supposed to be mean in your stories? In this story you will follow monsters to *Where the Wild Things Are*. There you will learn the real inside stories about your favorite monsters.

1. If you were a monster, what type of transportation would you use? List two everyday types of transportation and list three magical types of transportation that you would use to move around in a story about you. Explain how you would use each type of transportation. Try to be creative in your thinking.

   a. Everyday Type _____

   Reason _____

   Everyday Type _____

   Reason _____

   b. Magical Type _____

   Reason _____

   Magical Type _____

   Reason _____

   Magical Type _____

   Reason _____

2. What three strange names would you give monsters in a scary story? _____
   _____   _____

3. Can you think of three less threatening names for monsters in a story? _____
   _____   _____

4. What is your favorite bedtime tale? _____
   Does it contain any monsters or evil characters? _____

5. When you were young did you find it easier to fall asleep while being read a good book? ___

6. If you were writing a children's book, where would you hide monsters in it? _____

7. What kind of suit should a young boy wear if he is going out to look for monsters and wild things? _____

8. Are monster sounds in a story enough to scare the average child? What sounds would you have fierce monsters make? _____

9. If you wanted monsters to be less frightening, what kind of sounds would you give them?
   _____

10. List ten real animals that would make a scariest animal list? _____
    _____
    _____

Just the Facts

1. What was the first thing that grew in Max's room? _____

2. What were the two things that Max hung on the clothesline in his bedroom? _____

3. What did Max make in his wolf suit? _____

4. Max's nickname was _____.

5. Who gave this nickname to Max? _____

6. Max was sent to his bedroom without _____.

7. The ocean tumbled a _____ into Max's room.

8. How long did Max travel? _____

9. "Gnashed" describes what the wild things did with their _____.

10. What did the wild things do with their *eyes* to try to scare Max as he was landing on their

    island? _____

11. Two words calmed the monsters down. What were these two words? _____

12. The magic trick Max knew involved _____ into the wild things eyes and not blinking.

13. The wild things made Max their _____.

14. What did Max start on the island? _____

15. What feeling did Max have after sending the wild things off to bed without their supper?

    _____

16. Far away across the world, Max smelled good things to _____.

17. The wild things didn't want Max to leave their island? Why? _____

18. What was growing from the ceiling in Max's room? _____

19. Waiting for Max in his room when he returned was his _____

20. The condition that his supper was in was _____.

21. What was the color of the wolf suit that Max wore on his journey to find the wild things?

    _____

What Is Your Opinion?

Use the back of this paper to expand your ideas on each topic presented below.

1. Do you think it is proper to send young children to bed without any supper? Explain.

   _____

   _____

2. Max sailed for over a year to find the wild things' island. In all this time he never took his wolf suit off. Do you think this is strange? How could he have protected his wolf suit while sailing on the high seas? If he never took it off, it must have really smelled. What do you think? _____

   _____

3. If you were to ask children of all ages about their favorite clothing, do you think more kids would pick a dress-up sort of wear, or do you think they would choose knock-around wear as their favorite? Take a short survey before answering this question. _____

   _____

4. Where do you think Max's parents thought Max was when they brought the food to the room that he was supposed to be in as sort of a punishment?_____

   _____

5. The wild things met Max only once. Do you think the monsters made Max their king too quickly? Explain. _____

   _____

6. What kind of magic could a little boy possibly have that would allow him to bring the wild things under his spell? Where do you think he first found this magic? Make up a situation where he would have to use his magic again. _____

   _____

   _____

7. Was it a good thing to have a rumpus so soon after calming the wild things down? Why would you have had a rumpus?_____

   When wouldn't you have had a rumpus?_____

   _____

8. What are some of the things that could happen to a sailor who sails alone? _____

   _____

9. What did you think of the dragon that almost ate Max's boat? _____

   _____

10. What are the good and bad things about having a forest in your room? _____

   _____

GA1430

Three, Four, Five and Six Categories
Drills for Skills

Your topical knowledge will be tested in this activity. Each activity topic must be completed in thirty seconds. (Teachers may extend this time depending on the difficulty of the topic. Teams of two can also be used.) Your teacher will give you a topic. For example, Sea Creatures; you have thirty seconds to record a sea creature that has three letters, one that has four letters, a five-letter creature, as well as, a six-letter one.

Example:
Topic A: Sea Creatures
3. eel
4. crab
5. whale
6. shrimp

Topic B: Insects
3. _____
4. _____
5. _____
6. _____

Topic C: Trees
3. _____
4. _____
5. _____
6. _____

Topic D: Clothing
3. _____
4. _____
5. _____
6. _____

Topic E: Games
3. _____
4. _____
5. _____
6. _____

Topic F: Boy's Name
3. _____
4. _____
5. _____
6. _____

Topic G: Girl's Name
3. _____
4. _____
5. _____
6. _____

Topic H: Body Part
3. _____
4. _____
5. _____
6. _____

Make up some "three to six" categories of your own or try these additional suggestions: cars, famous people, colors, food, stores, computer terms, famous authors or movies.

Three to Six

33

GA1430

All-Purpose Vocabulary Hunt
Vexing Vocabulary I

One of the goals of teaching vocabulary is to ready children for words that they will meet every day in the "real world." This activity can be used with any story. You are to select/record fifteen key vocabulary words from the story. Then choose one word and indicate where you would come in contact with this word in the places listed below. Be sure to circle your selected vocabulary word. Be specific where it was found in each place.

Book title: _____

Fifteen Selected Words

_____	_____	_____	_____	_____
_____	_____	_____	_____	_____
_____	_____	_____	_____	_____

Place	**Specific Description of Word Usage**
bakery	_____
sporting event	_____
TV Guide	_____
pizza shop menu	_____
new car ad	_____
game directions	_____
report card comments	_____
ice-cream stand	_____

Teacher Note: This is an ongoing activity that we play like a scavenger hunt. The children have to verify finding the vocabulary word they selected. It is getting harder to give them new places to discover words. We also play a version of this game called Stumper. Each child picks a place where you find lots of words but where, you are predicting, children won't find many of their own vocabulary words. We write each place down and then proceed with our hunt. My favorite suggestion was "a milk carton."

All-Purpose Vocabulary Hunt
Vexing Vocabulary II

One of the goals of teaching vocabulary is to ready children for words that they will meet every day in the "real world." Hopefully, child and teacher will be able to enhance these words by finding synonyms and antonyms that are more powerful than the original words. This activity can be used with any story. You are to select/record fifteen key vocabulary words from the story. Then you are to indicate where you would come in contact with an antonym or synonym for this word in the places listed below. Be sure to circle your selected vocabulary word and place it next to the synonym/antonym that you found. Be specific where it was found in each place.

Book title: _____

Fifteen Selected Words

_____ _____ _____ _____ _____

_____ _____ _____ _____ _____

_____ _____ _____ _____ _____

Place	Specific Description of Word Usage
McDonald's	_____
famous poem	_____
shoe store	_____
shirt wash label	_____
post office	_____
video store	_____
comic book	_____
iced tea can	_____

Teacher Note for Weekend Travel: This is an ongoing activity that we play like alphabetical car billboards. The children have to verify finding the vocabulary word they selected. The word's opposite must be found on a billboard. We write each place we see the billboard and then proceed with our hunt. It is mind boggling how many children spot the same words on off-of-the-beaten-path billboards.

Ideas and Illustrations I

You have just purchased Wild Thing Island. You are on a trip there to redesign the island for your new home. Fill out the convenient questionnaire below before beginning any construction. On the next page show your blueprints and construction designs for your new buildings.

1. From whom was Wild Thing Island purchased?_____

   _____

2. What was the purchase price? _____

3. Did you take out a loan to purchase the property? _____

4. How many years do you have to pay back the loan? _____

5. What is the bank's name that holds your mortgage? _____

   _____

6. What is your real estate agent's name and company? _____

   _____

7. Where did you first hear about and see your island?_____

   _____

   _____

8. Draw a map showing the route from your town to the island.

   [ ]

9. What style of buildings will you have on the island? _____

   _____

10. Describe how the vegetation, trees and animal habitats will be protected during the new construction._____

    _____

    _____

11. How will you travel to the new island? What belongings will you be taking with you?_____

    _____

    _____

You have just purchased Wild Thing Island. You are on a trip there to redesign the island for your new home. Half of your new home, your new business and the island's amusement park has been constructed for you. Complete the second half of each drawing below before making a large scale model of your island.

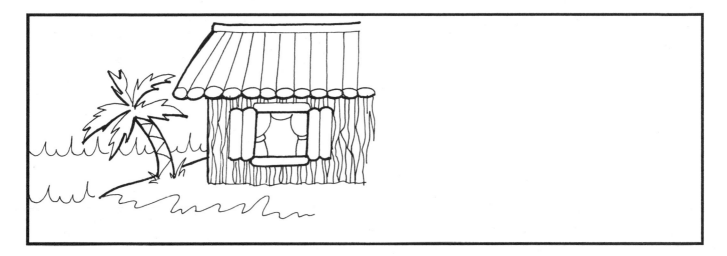

 # Wild Thing Mugs
Ideas and Illustrations III

Most malls have some type of computerized video setup that allows a particular store owner to print your favorite picture on buttons, newspapers, T-shirts, mirrors, coffee cups/mugs or baseball cards. Good advertising convinces parents that giving Grandma and Grandpa copies of the new baby's picture or the family's picture on a set of cards, mugs or buttons is cute and inexpensive. Companies are putting little leaguers on their own baseball cards to give to family members. You can see how a five-hundred-member little league team, each buying ten pictures, makes this a very profitable business. Some schools even have this same type of setup in their computer laboratories and use it as a money-making activity.

You are about to enter the mug-making business. Below are four strips like the ones used by a mug maker to make a lasting picture on a coffee mug. Complete the scene on each strip. Then use transparent tape and place the strip on a coffee cup that you have at home. On the back of this paper, create four strips for your own ideas.

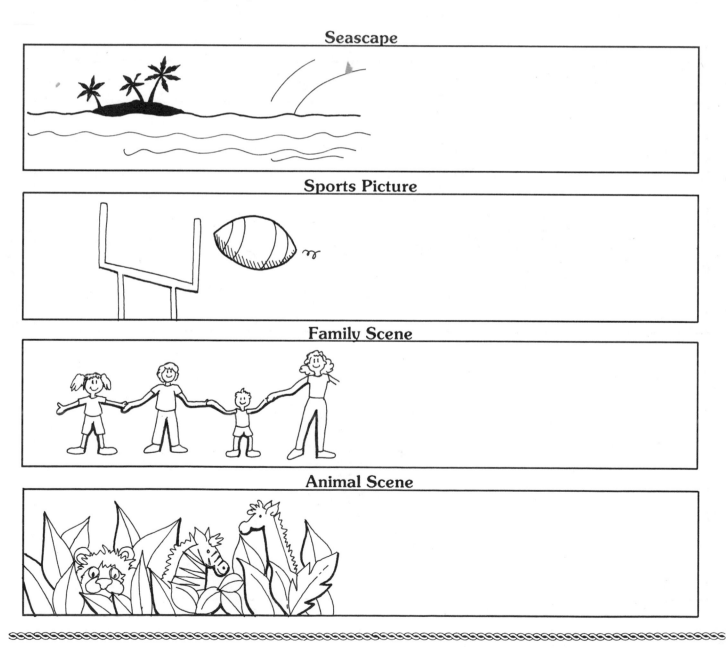

Seascape

Sports Picture

Family Scene

Animal Scene

GA1430

Mr. Muguire's Mug
Short-Term Project

You are now the proud owner of a mug making and decal shop. Students may prefer to be owners of surfboard and decal shops. Sitting on the shelves below are four mugs and the types of designs customers want you to put on them. Complete your best drawings on the mugs below. Cut out your two best ones and mount them on giant mugs next to your classmates' best mugs. Write a short description of your two best mugs, so a potential customer has an idea of what he or she is buying.

Birthday Cup

Wild Design

Description:

Description:

Sports Scene

Flowers

Description:

New Mug Idea

GA1430

Student Suggestions

1. Imagine that *Where the Wild Things Are* is a television program. It is your job to write three different commercials focusing on the Wild Thing line of candy, clothes, toys, jewelry, boats or wallpaper. Pick another item to sell during the program if these don't appeal to you. Whatever you select must somehow follow the theme of the story.

2. Write the king's oath that the wild things have Max say during his king crowning ceremony.

3. Draw a map or time line chronicling Max's journey throughout the book.

4. Create a monster's baseball team selecting monsters from fact or fiction to play each position. Please indicate why you selected each creature for the particular assignment.

5. Make a Moms' Nicknames for Kids poster. Highlight the silly and embarrassing things moms call their children.

6. Write a poem called "Lonely No More." In it show children two or three ways to overcome loneliness.

7. Design a parade float or model that might have been included in Max's rumpus parade.

8. Design three crowns that Max might have worn sailing, playing ball, meeting with the king's court or eating. Give each crown two special features that would make the crown perfect for what Max was doing at that time.

9. Cut out pictures of boats and make a boat catalog or collage. Research three children's stories where boats play an important part in the outcome of the story.

10. Mischief night before Halloween has become a national disgrace in many cities (Detroit, Michigan; Camden, New Jersey). Research this phenomenon and find out what these cities are doing to curb this uncalled for rash of destruction.

11. Create a short-term project of clothesline ideas that your class can hang up in the classroom like Max hung up in his room.

12. Cut out the eyes of various creatures and mount them on a 3" x 5" (7.62 x 12.7 cm) card. Have your classmates guess each animal or well-known person displayed. We do this in a peephole activity. Fold a piece of paper in half. Open it and paste a picture on the right-hand side. Close the paper and cut a hole through the top portion so you can see only part of the picture. From this small peek have your students guess what each picture is.

40

Teacher Suggestions

1. Video T-shirts, jeans and mugs can be found at every mall. Invite a video T-shirt maker to your school for a classroom demonstration. Talk to your local computer expert about the equipment needed to teach this same type of lesson using your own school computers and borrowed equipment.

2. Have your class design King of the Wild Things flags that Max could fly over his boat. Place them on a clothesline near your window for an excellent display.

3. One of the teachers in my school made a magic carpet out of big pieces of butcher block paper. She then had everyone write a story and illustrate a picture about where he would like this magic carpet to take him. She pinned these writings and drawings to the carpet and hung the carpet up like a giant wall tapestry. It is a real eye-catcher at the second or seventh grade level. This same thing can be done with a giant wall hanging of Max's boat. Attach to it the writings and drawings of your class as to where they would go in search of wild things.

4. Have a calm Wild Thing contest where the children must dress up, draw pictures or make dioramas as close to the scenes and characters in the story as possible.

5. One of the national ideas in Olympics of the Mind a few years back was to take a famous drawing, build it with drawings, people and scenery, then bring it to life. Using this same technique, see if you and your class can duplicate a scene from a book favorite and bring it to life in music or drama.

6. Make a suggestion of "Things Monsters Can Do to Keep out of Trouble" poster contest with your students.

7. Have your students create a dance called the Rumpus.

8. Organize a "Supper Should Never Be Taken Away from a Child" debate. Have your students write both sides of the issue before presenting the side they truly support.

9. Take a hot and cold survey with your students. Have them select five things that they feel are better hot and five things that they feel are better cold. Combine their selections. How many things made both lists? Follow this up with the things that are just as good hot or cold.

10. Organize a class wild things expedition–knapsacks, sleeping bags and all. Focus your math, social studies, geography, reading, science and literature on this classroom quest. Have the class write periodic radio broadcasts that can be given during the day to report on the various operation stages, as well as the success of the operation.

41

GA1430

Write Like a Master

The story starters below have a theme of a person who seems to be searching for something. Try to make his search serious, humorous or unbelievable.

Story Starter I

I've looked everywhere. One minute this wild thing with straight hair is in front of me, the next my sister is standing in the very same spot the creature was just a split second ago. Maybe this can be sorted out by _____

_____

_____

Story Starter II

You are looking at the most amazing creatures ever found on a single expedition. The Greeldi Forest and River have been untouched by humans. I first discovered the forest and its hidden river by accident. I _____

_____

_____

Story Starter III

My classmates call me "Mr./Mrs. Nowhere to Be Found." Every time we go on a class trip I get lost. I don't do this on purpose. It just seems that every time I turn around to look at something in a museum or at an animal farm, my class line disappears. My mother says Uncle Raphael had a similar problem. He _____

_____

_____

Story Starter IV

I have one transfer token left but two transfers to make. What would Max, King of the Wild Things, do in a situation like this? Wrong! You can't eat the bus driver. Then who will drive the bus? I need one of those creative answers my teacher talks about. She always says they will make her proud. Hope she likes this idea because _____

_____

_____

Story Starter V

Write a wild thing story starter of your own in the space provided. See if you can get two classmates to add to your story starter.

_____

_____

_____

GA1430

Gameboard

Materials Needed: Two number cubes, movers, light-colored crayons; Vexing Vocabulary; Just the Facts. Student-made and teacher-made question cards can be placed in the areas provided for them on the gameboard. They are optional but highly recommended. A card is picked each time a player has a multiple of five points in his/her bank (5, 10, 15, 20 or 25).

Players Needed: Two to four players or teams of two players

Play Procedures: Players alternate turns; throw number cubes; move in either direction at any time. This allows for playing strategies, rather than just mindlessly moving around a gameboard.

The Roll: Roll both number cubes. Your teacher will tell you to conduct some math operations with the number cubes. The three rules used most often in my classroom are

(a) Subtract the smaller from the larger; then move that many spaces (6 - 4 = 2). Move two spaces.

(b) Multiply the two cubes and move the number of spaces in the one's column of the answer (2 x 6 = 12). Move two spaces.

(c) Keep on adding the two cubes until you get one digit as the answer (6 + 6 = 12, 12 = 1 + 2 = 3). Move three spaces. Mathematicians call this finding the digital root.

Object: To score twenty-five points or to capture wild things, animals, furnishings or sailboats. Owning wild things, animals, furnishings or sailboats can be accomplished by landing on them in a normal turn, trading for them when you land on a trading post or buying one of them for two times their value when you land on the bank. Each time you land on a property, you color in (or initial) the little block in the corner of the property and put the points in your running bank. Ownership will change after trades only. Cross them out on the score sheet and add them to the other column. A scoreboard is provided for you. Each time someone lands on your property, he must pay you the number of points indicated in the top right-hand corner. Each time you land on your own property, you receive twice the points shown.

Winning Sets: Wild things (one, two, three and four); animals (rabbit, wolf, lamb and chipmunk); furnishings (bed, night-light, rug and dresser); sailboats (A, B, C and D)

Player One's Properties/Score	Player Two's Properties/Score

Game Card Property Pieces

On this page are the sixteen game pieces for *Where the Wild Things Are*. Cut them out and place them on oaktag to prolong their usability. Place a little box next to the gameboard as a storage area. Each time someone lands on an appropriate board space, he receives points and one of the game cards to verify property ownership. It also makes property trading much easier. The next time you play the game, design your own game card property pieces. Design a gameboard and create your own educational board game. Pick a theme. Then try to add important facts and intellectual flavor to your game.

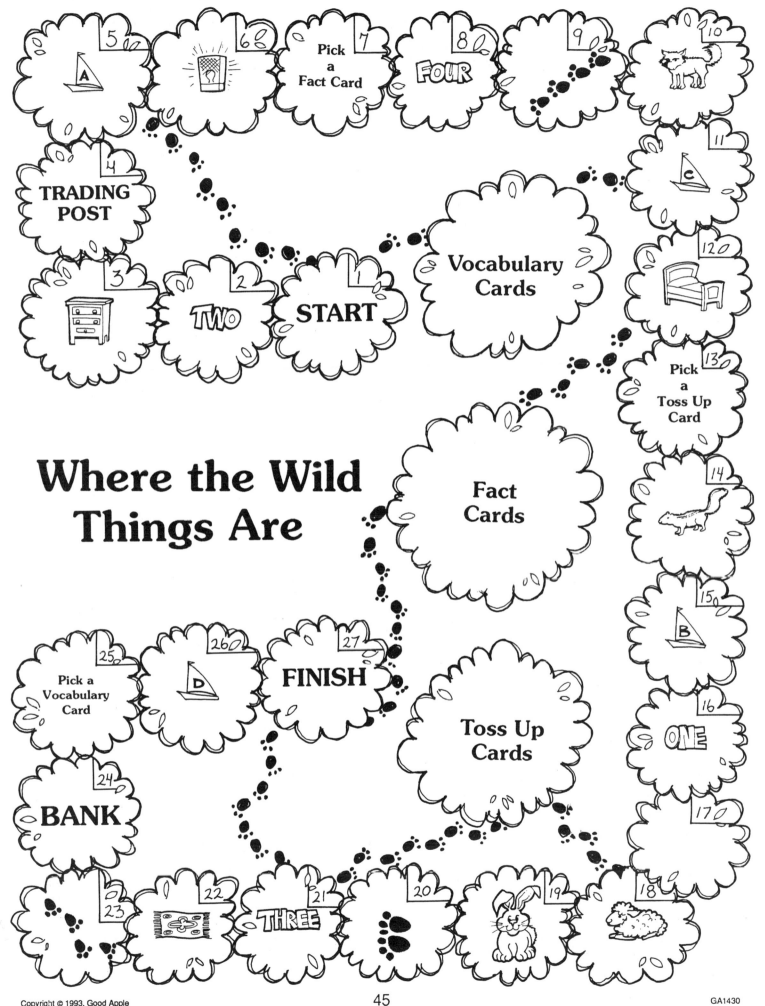

Where the Wild Things Are

45

GA1430

GA1430

Lead-Ins to Literature

Are you tired of seeing shootings, fights, crashes and wars in children's books and on television? A group of librarians and thirty-three of our best authors and illustrators feel the same way. They got together to write a book showing the meaning of peace and the horrors of war. Their stories are serious and humorous. The authors, through pen and picture, call for individual, neighborhood and world harmony. They ask each of us to celebrate peace and work on the hope that every child inherit a peaceful world. All the money raised from the purchase of this book goes to organizations striving to make a peaceful world. After reading this book, it is this author's hope that you will tell a friend to buy and read it.

1. You are asked to attend a children's conference on world peace. What three useful ideas would you bring to this meeting?

   a. _____

   b. _____

   c. _____

2. Ask three friends the same question. Record their best ideas in the spaces below.

   Friend One's Name_____

   Friend One's Best Idea _____

   Friend Two's Name_____

   Friend Two's Best Idea _____

   Friend Three's Name _____

   Friend Three's Best Idea _____

3. Do you find that more of your friends like violent happenings in their stories, or do you have more friends that would rather not see these types of things in books? Explain.

   _____

   _____

   _____

4. Do you think a child that sees constant fighting in his/her home or neighborhood has a chance to grow up a peaceful and peace-loving person? How could this be possible?

   _____

   _____

   _____

Use the back of this paper to respond to these questions: What do you know about Greenpeace? Has there ever been a peace march/vigil/religious service in your town? Have you read *The Wall* or *Sadako and the Thousand Paper Cranes*? What books have you read that express the peace theme?

What Is Your Opinion?

1. Why do you think so many authors and illustrators donated their skills to have this book published? _____

   _____

   _____

2. Have you read any other stories or books by the authors that were featured in this book? List the books and authors, please. _____

   _____

   _____

3. One of Maurice Sendak's wild things is on the front cover of the book. The wild thing has a bird's nest in its head. Why do you think this illustration is important to the whole theme of the book? _____

   _____

   _____

4. There are people who would object to this book. Write the objections you think they might have in criticizing this book. _____

   _____

   _____

5. Which story would most likely change a person's belief toward war? How and why? _____

   _____

   _____

6. "I Was There" is one of my favorites in this book. It made me think of all the times I could have been there but wasn't. What things in your life could you have been there for, yet you weren't? _____

   _____

   _____

7. Do you think more people would be influenced by a humorous approach to this topic, or do you feel a serious approach is more appropriate? Treat this like a mini debate and present both sides. _____

   _____

   _____

8. The illustrations in *The Big Book for Peace* cover many artistic styles. Compare and contrast two of your favorite and two of your least favorite illustrations. Attach your drawn copy of the illustration with your critical comments.

9. What is your opinion of the religious nature of the song "One More Time"? At what age do you think children are ready to discuss the being "carried away by death" verse? _____

   _____

GA1430

Vexing Vocabulary

It is amazing how many animal and creature names end with a complete word. You will find the word endings of animals below. See if you can find the beginning to complete the animal. In column two, try to find an ordinary everyday word that also has the same ending.

Animal Ending/Full Name	**Everyday Word**
Example: it/rabbit	habit
1. or _____	_____
2. an_____	_____
3. key_____	_____
4. arrow_____	_____
5. bra _____	_____
6. ant _____	_____
7. on _____	_____
8. in _____	_____
9. evil_____	_____
10. rot _____	_____
11. ark _____	_____
12. low_____	_____
13. ken_____	_____
14. oar _____	_____
15. us _____	_____
16. ear _____	_____
17. her _____	_____

Can you find six additional animals that end in a word? Record your animal endings below. Write the correct answer on a separate piece of paper. Exchange your work with a friend.

1. _____ _____   _____
2. _____ _____   _____
3. _____ _____   _____
4. _____ _____   _____
5. _____ _____   _____
6. _____ _____   _____

How many countries can you find that end in a word?

_____

_____

GA1430

The Two Brothers
Facts and Opinions

1. How far apart were the two brothers' castles? _____

2. Who gave them their small kingdom?_____

3. The two brothers sealed their agreement by embracing each other and by_____.

4. Pebbiaw grumbled about the bottomless pit that his brother had for a stomach. He called him a _____.

5. Ninniaw's dinner feast included roast venison and what three game birds? _____

   _____ _____

6. What two additional birds did Pebbiaw include in his lavish affair that were not in his brothers? _____

7. Who were described as hot-headed fellows? _____

8. To stop a possible band of ruffians from spying on his castle, what did Pebbiaw do? _____

   _____

9. What wasn't worth carving?_____

10. Which brother was dim-witted? _____

1. Do you think it was the father's fault that his two sons never learned how to get along with each other? Who would you blame for their actions? Why? _____

   _____

   _____

2. The brothers could have kept the original castle, and maybe the trouble between them would never have started. What then could they have done to make their relationship work? _____

   _____

   _____

3. Do you find that the brothers you know have more trouble getting along than the sisters you know? Explain. _____

   _____

   _____

4. Would you have suggested a third party to help the brothers solve all their problems? Why do you think so many people fear going to a third party for help with family problems?_____

   _____

   _____

5. What kind of reminder are the two piles of blackened stones? What kind of lesson should the brothers have learned from their shattered castles? _____

   _____

   _____

Law of the Great Peace
Facts and Opinions

1. What did people sit on under the great tree of peace? _____

2. Where did the great white roots spread to? _____

3. How many nations were originally included in the League of Nations? _____

4. Two words described the nature of the great white roots. What were these two words?

   _____   _____

5. Other _____ nations or _____ nations are welcome to seek refuge among the five nations and are persuaded to accept the great peace.

6. Who made the Indians of blood and soil? _____

7. What was cast into the depths of the earth? _____

8. Where was strife cast? _____

9. What happened to the tallest tree? _____

10. Name the five Indian tribes of the great nation. _____

   _____

1. The Great Peace was first written in the 1500's. It is still followed today? What do you give credit to for this lasting agreement? _____

   _____

2. What do you think would happen if everyone in the world buried all their armament? _____

   _____

   _____

3. How would the world benefit if everyone was at peace with each other? _____

   _____

4. What do you think the tree represents to the five nations? If you picked another symbol which had the same characteristics instead of a tree, what would that symbol be? Why? ____

   _____

   _____

5. Explain what an adapted book is? _____

   _____

6. Smoke is another important symbol to members of the five nations. What do you think the significance of smoke might be? _____

   _____

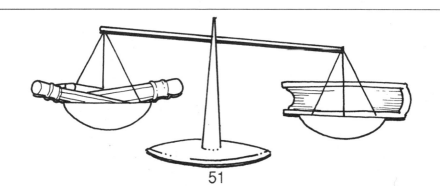

There Is an Island
Facts and Opinions

1. What does *sivuqaq* mean? _____

2. The legend says that St. Lawrence Island was planted in the _____.

3. Where were the races held that the men from St. Lawrence and Siberia attended?_____
   _____

4. "Seen the sun first" were words that were used to describe what tribe members? _____
   _____

5. What creature played the greatest importance to the survival of the Yupik people?_____
   _____

6. How long do the winter nights last?_____

7. The Yupiks remained a peaceful people in spite of the _____ around them.

8. What was used as the forbidden boundary between St. Lawrence and Siberia? _____
   _____

9. Tuesday, June 14, 1988, was the day that _____ took off.

10. Peace throughout the Arctic might lead to peace_____.

1. Is it possible to live on an island that has had only peace throughout its existence? _____
   _____
   _____

2. People always talk about saving the "old ways." Why are the old ways important to under
   standing each of our heritages and who people really are?_____
   _____

3. Why do you think it was important for the Yupik people to return part of the whale to the
   ocean? _____
   _____

4. The Russians passed a law forbidding anyone from visiting or leaving Siberia? What impres
   sions do you have of anyone that would pass such laws? _____
   _____
   _____

5. Can you describe the feelings of heartsick or homesick? _____
   _____

6. How powerful can a letter possibly be? _____
   _____

GA1430

Seeing Double
Drills for Skills I

So you think you have mastered every type of vocabulary challenge thrown at you, "Bucko"? Ha! "Seeing Double" will fix you. The first clue will give you a word that has a double letter in it. The second clue will be what is left of the word when the double letter is removed. This also will be a word when you push the remaining letters together.

Clue 1/Clue 2   **Answer 1/Answer 2**

Example: Robert for short/not a girl   Bobby/boy

1. flower part/flowers in spring   _____

2. watering hole/two of us   _____

3. a fruit/ginger _____ soda   _____

4. masked avenger/city animal habitat _____

5. calm/cat sound   _____

6. large fights/hay is wrapped into   _____

7. snake sound/*hello*, for short   _____

8. home run great/Ronald, shortened   _____

9. good looking/animal food   _____

10. father/part of a week   _____

11. queen's daughter/queen's son   _____

12. mountaintop/you wear a tie with it _____

13. bang a pillow/winter "bug" (disease) _____

14. throws/ten foot parts   _____

15. horse equipment/shopping money saver _____

16. make a sport's comeback/sun's beam   _____

17. happen/belonging to us   _____

Five spaces have been provided for your best "seeing double" clues and answers. Let your clues challenge your classmates.

1. _____   _____

2. _____   _____

3. _____   _____

4. _____   _____

5. _____   _____

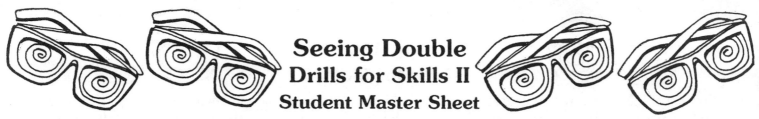

Seeing Double
Drills for Skills II
Student Master Sheet

After completing the "Seeing Double" work sheet on the previous page, did you ask yourself how many letters of the alphabet that appear as doubles can be removed from a word and still leave a word? Of course, you didn't. That is why this challenge sheet has been designed. The twenty-six letters of the alphabet are listed for you. See how many of the letters could be used in this activity. The combinations of JJ, WW, XX, UU, HH and ZZ should be next to impossible, but we've given you help on some of the others. See how many you can complete. Then vote with your classmates as to whose selection for each letter is most unique.

A. _____   _____
B. _____   _____
C. _____   _____
D. _____   _____
E. _____ feeling _____   _____ fling _____
F. _____   _____
G. _____   _____
H. _____   _____
I. _____   _____
J. _____   _____
K. _____   _____
L. _____ collins _____   _____ coins _____
M. _____   _____
N. _____ funnel _____   _____ fuel _____
O. _____   _____
P. _____   _____
Q. _____   _____
R. _____   _____
S. _____   _____
T. _____   _____
U. _____   _____
V. _____   _____
W. _____   _____
X. _____   _____
Y. _____   _____
Z. _____   _____

An easier version of this game is finding two words that have double *A*'s, *B*'s and so on through the alphabet.

GA1430

One Great Game
Drills for Skills III

You will find that this is "one great game." Use the clues below as they lead you to discover words that have *one (o-n-e)* in them in exact order. After you finish the challengers below, try to find words that have the letters *t-w-o* in them. They do not have to be in order. If you find one that has the two in order, like **footwork** or **outworked**–the steel company **outworked** all their competitors–have your teacher put them in a special list. After finding the clue word, find out what fraction of the word remains if you took the *o-n-e* out.

Clue	Answer	Problem
Example: ice-cream holder	cone	1/4
1. finished		
2. separated feeling		
3. the working bee		
4. granite is one		
5. long distance tool		
6. dog food		
7. frontiersman Daniel		
8. disappeared		
9. hive product		
10. truthful		
11. musical fund		
*12. a look-alike		
13. lying flat		

Can you find five *o-n-e* words that weren't covered above?

1. _____
2. _____
3. _____
4. _____
5. _____

"one great game"

GA1430

Short-Term Projects I

You have been asked to give the opening speech at the first children's Worldwide Peace Conference. Record your opening remarks below.

_____

_____

_____

_____

_____

_____

At this conference you are the head of a committee that is discussing the world's three most pressing peace problems. What three problems do you think your committee should discuss?

_____

_____

_____

Can you find three famous quotes that pertain to the peace issue? List the person and his/her quote below. Place an illustration under each quote.

Person _____ Quote _____

```



```

Person _____ Quote _____

```



```

Person _____ Quote _____

```



```

Summarize the things that this first peace conference accomplished, and indicate some after-conference activities that will continue to promote the cause of peace worldwide.

_____

_____

 GA1430

Short-Term Projects II

What do you know about the Nobel Peace prize and the accomplishments of some of its winners?

1. When is the Nobel Peace prize given?

_____

2. What country/organization gives the Nobel Peace prize?

_____

3. Where do the monetary funds come from for this prize?

_____

4. What are the requirements for receiving this award?

_____

5. What type of monetary reward is attached to the peace prize?

_____

Research three of the last five Nobel Peace prize winners. Record the names, accomplishments (reasons why given the award) and draw illustrations of the winning accomplishment in the space provided. The author prefers that each person that you highlight be allotted a full sheet of paper. Each award winner and your illustration can then be hung on a bulletin board as sort of a peace "hall of fame." Use the space below for your preplanning.

Person	Accomplishment	Event Illustration

Person	Accomplishment	Event Illustration

Person	Accomplishment	Event Illustration

GA1430

Peace Conference Invitation
Ideas and Illustrations I

You have been asked to design the invitation for the first Worldwide Children's Peace Conference. Choose your words carefully and then place your illustration on the card below. The card already has two doves and two olive branches in its corners. Add your artwork around your writing. If you choose not to have these pictures on your card, use the back of this paper for your original greeting and illustrations. Make a classroom invitation clothesline.

Peace Conference Invitation

Research the appearance of the Nobel, Newbery and Caldecott medals. Then in the box below draw a peace medal that is named after you.

Your Imaginary Peace Accomplishments

_____

_____

_____

_____

Illustrate your most noteworthy accomplishment on another sheet of paper.

GA1430

The Birds' Peace
Ideas and Illustrations II

This is the story of a young girl whose father just went off to war. She bursts out of the house and into the woods where she tries to share her troubles with birds that, of course, can't communicate with her. After watching birds interact and listening to their songs of territorial rights, she realizes how disputes can be avoided. The story is a short four pages, yet it offers a great many images to the artistic eye. Make a sketch below of nine of the key visual pictures in the story. Enlarge your best drawing for a bulletin board entitled "Birds Can Teach Humans About Peace." Use colored pencils when drawing your pictures below.

Bird's Nest	Lean-To	Splotched Eggs

Purling Stream	Raspberry Bush	Bird on a Twig

Wooden Bridge	Maple Leaf/Tree	Busy Meadow

Make three additional boxes on the back of this page and make three additional sketches that this short story brings to mind. If you would like a real challenge, try drawing Kristy's hand as she is writing to her father; imitate Ted Rand's two illustrations for this story; or draw a picture of Kristy's father receiving her first letter.

Drive-In Book Window
Ideas and Illustrations III

Tired of waiting in lines at your local bookstore or library for the book you want? Then try _____ (your name) Book Window. It works like the drive-in window at your local hamburger stand. When you drive in you will see a menu of books on your left. A book server will say "hello" and ask you for your selections. Your job is to finish this picture, list the ten selections on the billboard on the left and write some of the things a book server might say about today's choices.

60

Teacher Suggestions

1. **Greenpeace** information can be obtained by calling 202-462-1177 (Washington, D.C.) or by writing Greenpeace
   1436 U Street NW
   Suite 201
   Washington, D.C. 20009

2. Amnesty International Information can be obtained by calling 1-800-552-6637.

3. The library is loaded with books on paper folding. Invite a paper folding expert to your classroom. Make paper cranes and send them to American school children on bases in Japan or to a Japanese classroom. Write to your local consul, service base or recruiting officer for mailing suggestions. Maybe you'll get lucky and have someone in your town attend a national peace rally. Ask him to distribute your paper cranes.

4. After reading *The Wall* by Eve Bunting to your class, plan an imaginary trip with your students to the Vietnam War Memorial in Washington, D.C. Find some members of your community that can be remembered on your trip. Include math activities, map skills, transportation schedules and the historical and geographical features of some of the towns you might use as stop-offs on your way. Discuss with the class ten things that you might leave at the wall and their significance to the family and person being remembered. Have your class research what the park service does with the thousands of things left at the memorial. Other cities have war memorials of their own. Visit your local memorial and research some of the people remembered there.

5. After Japan attacked the United States in 1941, war was voted on in Congress. One person voted against going to war, even after being attacked. Research with your class who this person was and what his reasons were.

6. Have a Hall of Peace design contest with your students. A peace museum is being placed in your town. Each of us (your students) is responsible for designing one room of the museum. Art students can work on each room's features and hall murals/drawings. Creative writers can write the room descriptions that will be heard on special earphones provided in each room.

7. Have your class write to the local USO to find out the types of services provided for service people overseas.

During the war everyone wrote to service men and women. Letters are needed now just as much. Start a peacetime writing campaign.

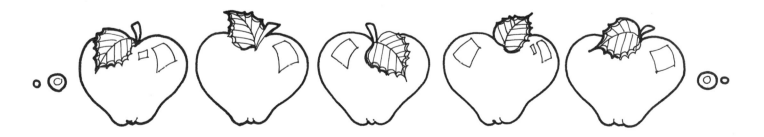

Write Like a Master

The following story starters concern the difficulties and hardships that peace activists must face in their many endeavors from worldwide peace to saving the forests, whales and environmental habitats worldwide. Put yourself in their place as you complete each story starter below. You have seen the humorous and serious blend of different authors that contributed to this book. See if you can write in the style of two of them.

Story Starter I

Hanging in this tree seemed like a good way to stop these loggers from chopping down these redwoods. But after three days of hanging here, I wonder if this is really worth it. There are only three of us doing this. Somehow, I thought there would be more. Every tree in this forest should have someone sitting in it. Don't people realize that each thing we lose _____

_____

_____

_____

Story Starter II

Save the whales! Someone is going to have to come out here and rescue us. As they say on television, "we are taking on water." We placed ourselves in front of the harpooneers and the whales, but they fired anyway. The blade hit us two feet below our waterline. Water is _____

_____

_____

_____

Story Starter III

This is my first New York Central Park peace rally. It is held every August on the date we dropped the first atomic bomb on Japan. People from Japan bring paper cranes made by Japanese school children to pass out to everyone at the rally. It made me think of _____

_____

_____

Story Starter IV

I am only eight years old, and this is the first time my mom has taken me to see my older brother's name on the Vietnam War Memorial in Washington, D.C. My mom started crying in the car before we even got there. Dad told me, "It's just women," but when we got to the wall and he touched my brother's name, his tears were twice as large as my mother's. I don't understand ___

_____

_____

GA1430

Gameboard

Materials Needed: Two number cubes, movers, light-colored crayons; Vexing Vocabulary; Just the Facts. Student-made and teacher-made question cards can be placed in the areas provided for them on the gameboard. They are optional but highly recommended. A card is picked each time a player has a multiple of five points in his/her bank (5, 10, 15, 20 or 25).

Players Needed: Two to four players or teams of two players

Play Procedures: Players alternate turns; throw number cubes; move in either direction at any time. This allows for playing strategies, rather than just mindlessly moving around a gameboard.

The Roll: Roll both number cubes. Your teacher will tell you to conduct some math operations with the number cubes. The three rules used most often in my classroom are

   (a) Subtract the smaller from the larger; then move that many spaces (6 - 4 = 2). Move two spaces.

   (b) Multiply the two cubes and move the number of spaces in the one's column of the answer (2 x 6 = 12). Move two spaces.

   (c) Keep on adding the two cubes until you get one digit as the answer (6 + 6 = 12, 12 = 1 + 2 = 3). Move three spaces. Mathematicians call this finding the digital root.

Object: To score twenty-five points or to capture four protest signs, peace methods, do withouts or world helpers. Owning protest signs, peace methods, do withouts or world helpers can be accomplished by landing on them in a normal turn, trading for them when you land on a trading post or buying one of them for two times their value when you land on the bank. Each time you land on a property you color in (or initial) the little block in the corner of the property and put the points in your running bank. Ownership will change after trades. Cross them out on the score sheet and add them to the other column. A scoreboard is provided for you. Each time someone lands on your property, he must pay you the number of points indicated in the top right-hand corner. Each time you land on your own property, you receive twice the points shown.

Winning Sets: Protest signs (Save Our Trees, Stop Pollution, Recycle and Conserve Energy); peace methods (peace symbols, peace rallies, protest songs and protest posters); do withouts (nuclear weapons, tanks, guns and warplanes); world helpers (plant a tree, vote, help the homeless, give to the needy)

Player One's Properties/Score	Player Two's Properties/Score

Game Card Property Pieces

On this page are the sixteen pieces for *The Big Book for Peace*. Cut them out and place them on oaktag to prolong their usability. Place a little box next to the gameboard as a storage area. Each time someone lands on an appropriate board space, he receives points and one of the game cards to verify property ownership. It also makes property trading much easier. The next time you play the game, design your own game card property pieces. Design a gameboard and create your own educational board game. Pick a theme. Then try to add important facts and intellectual flavor to your game.

GA1430

The Big Book for Peace

Fact Cards

Vocabulary Cards

Toss Up Cards

START

1 SAVE OUR TREES

2

3

4 PLANT A TREE

TRADE

5 PICK A TOSS UP CARD

6 VOTE

7 STOP POLLUTION

8 PEACE RALLY

9

BANK

10 PICK A VOCABULARY CARD

11 PROTEST SONGS

12

13 RECYCLE

14 GIVE TO THE NEEDY

PICK A FACT CARD

TRADE 15

16 CONSERVE ENERGY

17

18 PROTEST POSTERS

19 Help the Homeless

FINISH

GA1430

Higglety Pigglety Pop

Salami Mop Jennie's Travels Helpful Milkman

What a Play Suitcase Baby Acting Experience

Mother Goose Theater Star Lion

LUNCHCOUNTER OPEN

Acting Diploma

Happy Milkman

Lead-Ins to Literature

Did you ever see Mother Goose in person? The reason I am asking this is that everyone has heard this woman's rhymes, but no one has ever seen her. To make matters even worse, the World Mother Goose Theater, founded by Mother Goose, is putting on a production. They need a few good actors. Jennie, the dog, is on the way there for a tryout. She may never meet Mother Goose, but she meets enough characters to make this story very interesting.

1. If you were meeting Mother Goose for the first time, what would you call her? _____
   _____
   Why? _____

2. Your dog is leaving home to become an actor. What words of encouragement would you give him? _____
   _____

3. Describe the articles a pet might pack before a long trip. _____
   _____

4. What kind of parts could a dog have in an important stage production? _____
   _____

5. How can a dog gain stage experience if she has never performed on stage? _____
   _____

6. The author has a lion and a milkman in this dog story. What do you think they will have in common with Jennie, the dog?_____
   _____

7. What type of dog would you pick to star in a Mother Goose rhyme? Explain. _____
   _____

8. What Mother Goose rhyme is your favorite? Record a few lines below. Circle the key vocabulary words. Rhyme name: _____
   Key lines: _____
   _____

9. What kind of training do most stage animals receive?_____
   _____

10. What authors' poems are the closest to the Mother Goose rhymes that you learned when you were younger? _____
    _____

11. Have you ever seen the movie *Rock and Roll Mother Goose*? Illustrate and describe your thoughts on this show.
    _____
    _____

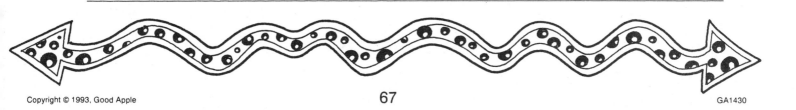

 GA1430

Just the Facts

1. Who did the parlormaid say was going to eat Jennie if she couldn't make the baby eat?

   _____

2. What kind of buckles did the black leather bag have? _____

3. Where did the baby throw the comb and brush? _____

4. What castle was mentioned in Jennie's note?_____

5. Why could the plant talk? _____

6. Sandwich boards were worn by what animals? _____

7. An ad came before "Call Ex 1-1212." Please neatly copy it here. _____

   _____

   _____

   _____

8. Jennie must get experience by _____ of the full moon.

9. As the pig was beginning to vanish, what type of sandwich was Jennie able to snatch?

   _____

10. Who played the character of the milkman?_____

11. How many nurses did the baby have before Jennie?_____

12. The bottle of skimmed milk was deliberately knocked over by _____.

13. What words followed *no* in the baby's vocabulary? _____

14. What kind of door did the lion take the baby through? _____

15. A great shower of leaves was created by the _____.

16. The stage was lit by what type of lights? _____

17. How many performances did Jenny perform on Saturdays? _____

18. Jennie's old master received a _____ from her.

GA1430

 **What Is Your Opinion? I**

1. Some books have animals talking to animals, while others have animals talking to humans. Which one do you prefer? Why? _____
_____

2. Can you think of three reasons an animal might want to leave home? _____
   a. _____
   b. _____
   c. _____

3. Maurice Sendak uses a milk wagon in the story. Most children have never seen one. Why would an author choose something that is so unrecognizable to most of his readers?
_____
_____

4. Did you find the lion to be a likable character or did his "eat everything" attitude seem unkind? _____
_____
_____

5. Create three ways that a dog could answer and sign his/her fan mail. _____
_____

6. If you were a dog's business agent, in what type of movies would you cast your client? See if you can find two outstanding and two ordinary roles for your client. _____
_____
_____

7. If you were creating an "animals only" production, what would your theme be? Do you think this theme would attract a large following? _____
_____

8. Would you pay your animal actors in food or money? If they were paid in money, how would you suggest they spend the money? _____
_____

9. In the old days milk was delivered at night? Why do you think this was necessary? _____
_____

10. How many dog actors can you name? (Lassie for starters)
_____   _____   _____

11. Where would you build a Mother Goose Theater? Why? _____
_____

GA1430

What Is Your Opinion? II

1. How important is experience to an actor or actress?_____
_____
_____

2. What was the best experience that Jennie received in the story?_____
_____

3. List three of the characters in the story from most helpful to least helpful. Give a brief note of explanation with each of your choices.

    a._____ _____

    b._____ _____

    c._____ _____

4. Would you have left a home that had everything? _____
_____

5. Why do you think Jennie was so mean to the potted plant?_____
_____

6. Being a "billboard person" doesn't seem like an easy job. Highlight the good and bad points of carrying a billboard all day. _____
_____
_____

7. Compare the billboard pig to the pig in *Charlotte's Web*. How are they alike/different?
_____
_____

8. Make a copy of Maurice Sendak's best illustration in this book.

9. In what ways is the lion in this story different from the lion in the book *The Lion, the Witch and the Wardrobe*? _____
_____

10. Can you think of any other part of the story that was stranger than all of the characters that Jennie met in her travels showing up for the stage production? _____
_____

GA1430

Vexing Vocabulary

raspberry	cellar	thermometer
nervously	yonder	twinkling
unraveled	vanilla	confident
jumping stomach	mayonnaise	blossom
experience	yogurt	deliberately
modestly	instead	staircase
dangling	oblige	miserably
discontented	fade	starlight

Your writing skills will be thoroughly tested by this vocabulary activity. Below you will find a letter that you are writing to your best friend. It has been started for you. Record a word in each blank. If it is a vocabulary word, you score ten points. Any other word is worth one point. The maximum score on this challenge is 143. See how close you come to this score.

Dear _____,

    I am sitting here in bed with a _____ in my mouth. _____ of the _____ I'd rather have a _____, but such is not my luck. No one will believe the _____ that I just had. My _____ _____ won't stop shaking. It all started when my dog, Burlap, was kidnapped. I found the ransom note on the _____ _____. As I look out my window for some sign of Burlap, the _____ _____ didn't cheer me up. _____ _____ _____ _____ _____. Every time I look at the _____ _____ in the refrigerator, a tear comes to my eye. It was Burlap's _____ _____. Writing about this situation is _____ _____ very _____. I have to stop now. Please write to me. I could _____ _____ _____ _____.

                  Your _____ friend,

                  Jennie

Compose a letter telling your friend that you feel better or write her reply to your letter. Use the same scoring. Record your letter on the back of this sheet.

An Important Body of Words
Drills for Skills

I don't think your teachers ever told you that knowing the parts of your body will help you increase your vocabulary. Each clue below will lead you to find a word that has a body part hidden in it. After you find the answer to the clue word, circle the body part hidden in it. Then find out what fraction of the whole word the body part is.

Clue	Answer/Hidden Body Part	Fraction
Example: shell carrier	snail	4/5
1. wake-up clock		
2. furniture for sitting		
3. sailing vessel		
4. toss a coin		
5. opposite of *poorest*		
6. rest on legs		
7. not late		
8. chocolate's color		
9. cloth hair ornament		
10. not behind		
11. *telling's* opposite		
12. Arnie, the golfer		
13. giant fireplace		
14. grave marker		
15. rubbing with nails		
16. French fries		
17. tiny splinter		

Can you find five words that will have each of these body parts hidden in them?

ear	head	arm
1.		
2.		
3.		
4.		
5.		

GA1430

Animal Actors and Their Agents
Short-Term Project I

You are the world's most brilliant animal agent. Your clients include every animal from Dumbo the elephant to Flipper the dolphin. Please put together a portfolio of your clients' pictures; then complete the following questionnaire concerning your animal client's talents and abilities to carry out many a challenging movie and theater role.

What type of animal have you brought us today? _____

What is your animal's name? _____

Does your client have any previous acting experience? _____

Please describe your clients three most challenging roles. Use the back of this paper if necessary.

_____

_____

_____

Draw a picture of your client's most interesting attribute.

[ ]

For what part is your client interviewing? _____

List your client's musical talents. _____

If the film or play involves stunts, does your client do his/her own stunts? _____

Is an hourly wage or full-time salary expected? _____

With whom did your client study? _____

Where? _____

Does your client hold any college or acting degrees? _____

Please name each of the institutions and the highest level of achievement in each one.

_____

Is your client willing to work out of the country? _____

What locations would he/she prefer? _____

List a humorous anecdote from your client's work experience. _____

_____

GA1430

 # Music Performance Review
Short-Term Project II

There are a great many songs that have been written which include an animal. From "Old Mac-Donald Had a Farm" to Pete Seeger's "Frog" song and video, local record shops are an animal's delight. Your task is to find an animal song to your liking and perform it for your classmates. You are to dress up, create props, illustrate and exhibit outstanding lip synchronization in the performance of your chosen song. Reproduce the rating sheet below for each person in the classroom. Your classmates will act as the judges of each performed work. Fill out the form below for your selection, as well as one of the selections of your classmates.

Your Selection

Your name_____

Your song _____

Original singer_____

First four lines of your song

_____

_____

_____

_____

Score You Think You Deserved in Each Area (from 1-100)

       Lip synchronization _____

       Props _____

       Artwork _____

       Costume _____

       Overall rating (1-100)_____

Friend's Rating

Name of student _____

Name of song _____

Original singer_____

       Lip synchronization _____

       Props _____

       Artwork _____

       Costume _____

       Overall rating (1-100)_____

Student Suggestions

1. Using "throwaway" material from your home, make a wind chime.

2. Using white paper, design a nurse's hat that is different for each day of the week.

3. Place the letters of the alphabet downward on a sheet of paper. For each letter of the alphabet list someone that would carry a black bag.

4. Not many areas have sandwich board advertising. See if you can find who still makes sandwich boards. What type of salary does a sandwich board carrier make? What do you feel makes sandwich board advertising impractical in most areas? What areas do you feel could benefit from sandwich board advertising?

5. Take a survey of your local delicatessens. See how many different types of cheeses and meats they carry? What do you predict is the most popular meat and cheese? Do this same thing for dog, cat and lion food.

6. What agency in your town handles the advertising posters for plays, movies and rock groups? Research the occupations that are important until the final product is made. Rank each of them according to salary. Include the advertising agency president as well as the typist and typesetter.

7. What is the closest museum to your house that features a children's book illustrator? Draw a split poster. On one side highlight your museum, on the other a museum of your choice.

8. The Mother Goose Theater playbill wasn't very creative or artistically attractive. Design a new playbill for the group's latest production. Find a playbill for something appearing in your town and re-create it in a new form.

9. One of the dullest parts of a theater is the stage curtain. Get a colored piece of cloth and design a stage curtain for your school or local theater. Why do you think stage curtains are so drab?

10. Make up five humorous suggestions for how to stop a lion from eating a baby.

11. Create three introductions for your best friend who just happens to be a lion: I want you to meet my "mane" man. You'll roar after meeting Donovan.

12. Create a 3-D poster on how yogurt is made.

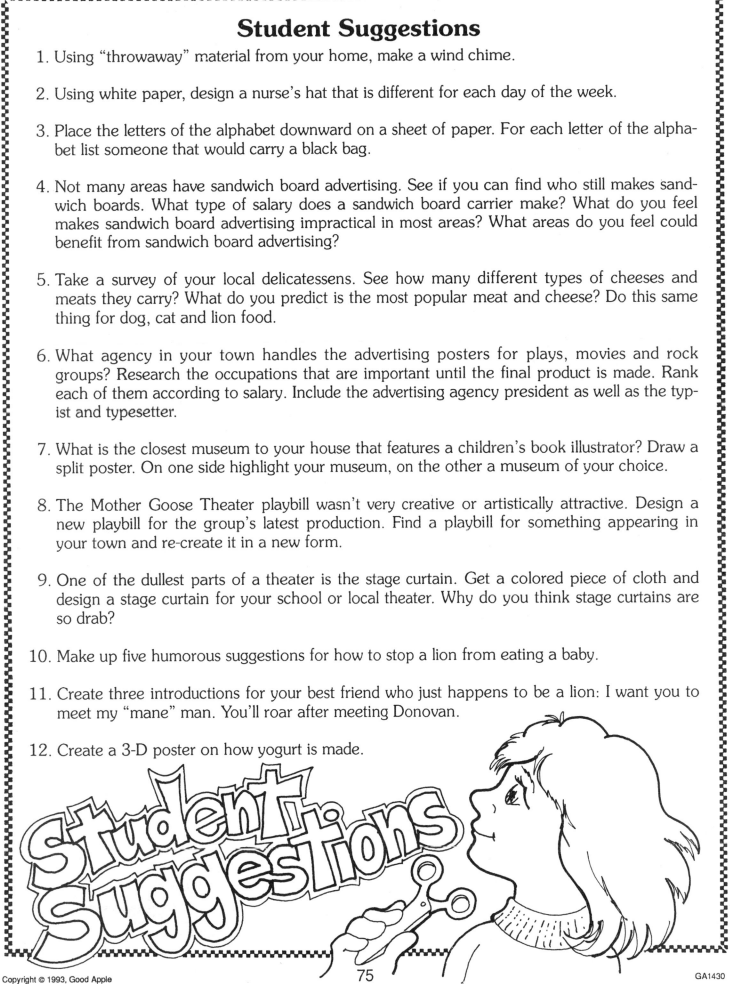

The Stranger
Write Like a Master

The theme for the story starters below revolves around an animal visitor to your house, school or job. The visitor could be Big Foot; the Loch Ness monster; or a talking cat, dog, mouse or animal of your choice.

Story Starter I

My story is an easy one. I learned how to talk at the mental health association's research facilities. They picked the smartest animals from around the world to be a part of their dolphin studies. They would try to get dolphins to speak and respond to symbols; then they would

_____

_____

_____

_____

Story Starter II

Watch it! I'm coming through–the world's only motorcycle riding bullfrog. I found this motorcycle on its side under the maple tree. The maple tree is next to the pond and I own the pond. Guess you can say that the motorcycle is mine. It was too big, at first. Now that I am older it is just right. It can reach speeds of _____ and can do all sorts of

_____

_____

Story Starter III

Mom and Dad won't let me have a pet, even though I really wanted one. So when I tapped on the dog's window at the pet store, and he tapped back and said, "Stop that," my teeth almost dropped out of my mouth. At first, I thought it was a recording that played after someone tapped the window. I was soon to learn otherwise. That innocent-looking dog could _____

_____

_____

Story Starter IV

Who was the most unforgettable animal that you have ever met? How old was this animal? What made this animal interesting or different from other animals and pets that you have had? Did this animal change your life or in some way make you a more caring and responsible person? How and why? _____

_____

_____

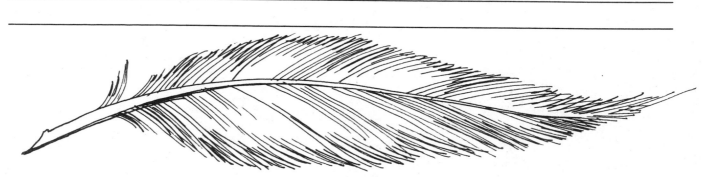

GA1430

Gameboard

Materials Needed: Two number cubes, movers, light-colored crayons; Vexing Vocabulary; Just the Facts. Student-made and teacher-made question cards can be placed in the areas provided for them on the gameboard. They are optional but highly recommended. A card is picked each time a player has a multiple of five points in his/her bank (5, 10, 15, 20 or 25).

Players Needed: Two to four players or teams of two players

Play Procedures: Players alternate turns; throw number cubes; move in either direction at any time. This allows for playing strategies, rather than just mindlessly moving around a gameboard.

The Roll: Roll both number cubes. Your teacher will tell you to conduct some math operations with the number cubes. The three rules used most often in my classroom are

(a) Subtract the smaller from the larger; then move that many spaces (6 - 4 = <u>2</u>). Move two spaces.

(b) Multiply the two cubes and move the number of spaces in the one's column of the answer (2 x 6 = 1<u>2</u>). Move two spaces.

(c) Keep on adding the two cubes until you get one digit as the answer (6 + 6 = 12, 12 = 1 + 2 = 3). Move three spaces. Mathematicians call this finding the digital root.

Object: To score twenty-five points or to capture four animals, stage props, milk or rules. Owning animals, stage props, milk or rules can be accomplished by landing on them in a normal turn, trading for them when you land on a trading post or buying one of them for two times their value when you land on the bank. Each time you land on a property you color in (or initial) the little block in the corner of the property and put the points in your running bank. Ownership will change after trades only. Cross them out on the score sheet and add them to the other column. A scoreboard is provided for you. Each time someone lands on your property, he must pay you the number of points indicated in the top right-hand corner. Each time you land on your own property, you receive twice the points shown.

Winning Sets: Animals (pigs, dogs, lions and cats); stage props (curtains, microphones, lights and backdrop); milk (baby bottle, milk carton, ice milk and milk wagon); baby-sitting rules (lock doors; no visitors; feed baby; and no lions, please)

Player One's Properties/Score	Player Two's Properties/Score

Game Card Property Pieces

On this page are the sixteen game pieces for *Higglety Pigglety Pop*. Cut them out and place them on oaktag to prolong their usability. Place a little box next to the gameboard as a storage area. Each time someone lands on an appropriate board space, he receives points and one of the game cards to verify property ownership. It also makes property trading much easier. The next time you play the game, design your own game card property pieces. Design a gameboard and create your own educational board game. Pick a theme. Then try to add important facts and intellectual flavor to your game.

78

Higglety Pigglety Pop

GA1430

What a Child
Pierre

Lead-Ins to Literature

In school we learn about caring for ourselves, our families, our home/country and the environment. What would happen if no one cared for any of these things? Would we all be monsters running all over the place on our own, or would we be humans living on an earth that was slowly being destroyed by people who didn't care about anything? You are going to meet a boy who doesn't even care if a lion eats him. We all have bad days, but having a lion eat me isn't something that I would want to happen to me. After a lion eats you, it is too late to learn how to care for things. Maybe reading about Pierre will show us some of the mistakes we all should avoid.

1. Where do you think people learn to care for themselves and others? _____
_____

2. If you were to take a survey, what three things do you think people care most about? What three things would they care least about? Please be ready to explain your top choices in both categories.
Care Most About
   a. _____
   b. _____
   c. _____

   Care Least About
   a. _____
   b. _____
   c. _____

3. What would cause a young child not to care about anything?
_____
_____

4. Can you name three books or movies that show the importance of caring? Describe the feature in each of the movies and books that stressed caring. _____
_____
_____
_____

5. I like the way the title sounds: Pierre, the boy that didn't care. Can you make up some other titles using children's names? For example, Mike, the boy that wouldn't hike; Joan, the girl that wouldn't phone; Jose, the boy that wouldn't play. _____
_____
_____

6. Name three things that you would be too late to do.
   a. _____
   b. _____
   c. _____

                    GA1430

Just the Facts

1. Did the story explain why Pierre didn't care? _____

2. What time did Pierre's parents return home? _____

3. Who was sick in bed? _____

4. If Pierre did not get off his head, where did his father say that he would march him to?

   _____

5. What word was used to describe the cream of wheat? _____

6. The story is designed to teach a _____.

7. Where was Pierre when the story started? _____

8. Who was pulled by the hair? _____

9. What did the doctor do to the lion? _____

10. Most mothers would probably be upset with Pierre for what he was pouring in his hair.

    What was he pouring in his hair, and where would you rather see it put? _____

11. What did Pierre have where his feet should have been? _____

12. Before the lion asked Pierre if he would like to die, where did the lion look? _____

    _____

13. What kind of lion paid a call to Pierre? _____

14. Where did Pierre return at half past nine? _____

15. How many people rode the lion back home? _____

16. What is the moral of the story? _____

17. Can you think of another word that means the same thing as *moral*? _____

18. How long was the lion a guest at Pierre's home? _____

19. When Pierre found out that he wasn't dead, what did he do? _____

20. Whose office was located in town? _____

21. What word describes the kind of shock that Pierre's parents received after he was eaten?

    _____

82

GA1430

What Is Your Opinion?

1. Do you think people will care more after reading this story? (Circle one.) yes/no. Explain your ideas. _____

   _____

2. Why do you think the lion is always pictured in children's stories as an animal that would eat children?_____

   _____

3. A folding chair is one of the things that I wouldn't want to be hit with over the head. Name three other things that wouldn't please the top of your head. Why?

   a. _____   _____

   b. _____   _____

   c. _____   _____

4. Can you think of three good reasons or benefits for standing on your head? _____

   _____

   _____

5. Pierre's parents tried to bribe him into caring. It was funny because if he cared, they would let him fold the folding chair. Surely there must be some better bribes than this to get a child to care! Can you name some bribes that are more reasonable?_____

   _____

   _____

6. How would you feel if your mother left you in the middle of a department store? What would you do? _____

   _____

7. How did you feel about Pierre's parents in the story? What were their good traits and what traits of theirs could be improved? _____

   _____

8. Even though he ate Pierre, I liked the lion in the story. How did you feel about the lion? Why? _____

   _____

9. Animals are often used as rides in children's parks? Do you approve of this? Give some reasons why this might be good for the animal and also why it might not be. _____

   _____

10. What would you have Pierre and the lion do in a follow-up story? _____

   _____

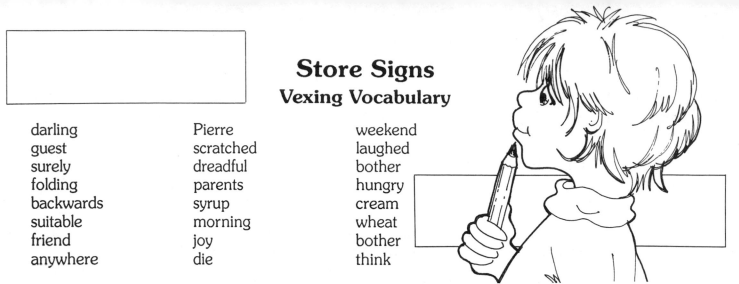

Store Signs
Vexing Vocabulary

darling	Pierre	weekend
guest	scratched	laughed
surely	dreadful	bother
folding	parents	hungry
backwards	syrup	cream
suitable	morning	wheat
friend	joy	bother
anywhere	die	think

You are a member of an advertising agency. You are to design the names of stores in your neighborhood. Each store name must have at least two vocabulary words in it. Circle them. In column one record your store's name. Column two will contain a description of what your store sells. In column three draw a mini picture of your store.

Store Name	Deals In	Illustration
Example:		
(Parents) (Think) Shop	Books for kids and adults	
(Anywhere) (Guest) Lodge	Overnight vacation resort	
(Hungry) (Cream) America	Ice-cream stand	

GA1430

 # Food Spelling
Drills for Skills I

There are many intelligent shortcuts that good spellers use to continue to increase their spelling vocabulary. One of those shortcuts is taught in *every* classroom in America. How many times have you heard your teacher, mom or dad tell you to look for smaller words in larger words? These smaller words will help you remember how the larger word is spelled. *Pierre*, the title of our story, has *pie* in it in exact order. Each item of food below, like the *pie* in *Pierre*, will help you remember a larger word. Examine the clue and write the correct word answer next to the clue.

Clue   **Larger Word**

Example: Remember the pea in cashew's friend.   peanut

1. A pear will help you to remember a weapon of war. _____

2. An apple will help you remember a bacon substitute. _____

3. A bean will help you remember this sea. _____

4. A jam-like spread will help you remember this fish. _____

5. A nut will help you remember a cake treat. _____

6. Corn will help you remember a street part. _____

7. A ham will help you remember a tool. _____

8. Rice will help you remember the cost. _____

9. A beet will help you remember an insect. _____

10. A clam will help you remember a gripping device. _____

11. A plum will help you remember a sink fixer. _____

12. A leek will help you remember something smooth and fast. _____

Write five "will help you remembers" of your own.

1. _____ will help you remember_____

2. _____ will help you remember_____

3. _____ will help you remember_____

4. _____ will help you remember_____

5. _____ will help you remember_____

"Look for smaller words in larger words."

GA1430

Alphabetical Opposites
Drills for Skills II

Your alphabetical ability will be tested as you try to think of a five-letter word that is the opposite of the clue. The clues on this sheet will steer you in the right direction. See if you can design a similar sheet. This time you and your classmates should look for synonyms as they go through clues and the letters of the alphabet.

Clue	**Opposite**	**Points**
Example: asleep	A <u>W</u> <u>A</u> <u>K</u> <u>E</u>	10
1. repair	B _ _ _ _	_____
2. foggy	C _ _ _ _	_____
3. enjoy	D _ _ _ _	_____
4. late	E _ _ _ _	_____
5. sink	F _ _ _ _	_____
6. poor	G _ _ _ _	_____
7. sad	H _ _ _ _	_____
8. outer	I _ _ _ _	_____
9. jam	J _ _ _ _	_____
10. stand	K _ _ _ _	_____
11. liked	L _ _ _ _	_____
12. stayed	M _ _ _ _	_____
13. south	N _ _ _ _	_____
14. desert	O _ _ _ _	_____
15. uproot	P _ _ _ _	_____
16. king	Q _ _ _ _	_____
17. unprepared	R _ _ _ _	_____
18. stupid	S _ _ _ _	_____
19. tender	T _ _ _ _	_____
20. bind	U _ _ _ _	_____
21. audio	V _ _ _ _	_____
22. fairy	W _ _ _ _	_____
23. pictures	X _ _ _ _	_____
24. ancient	Y _ _ _ _	_____
25. bland	Z _ _ _ _	_____

Score total _____

Score ten points for each clue and answer that starts with the same letter. Score one point for all other answers. Total your score on the line provided.

GA1430

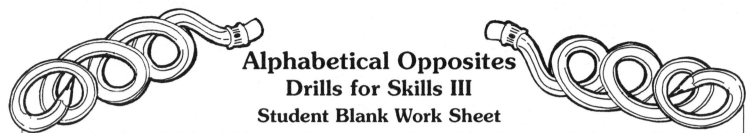

Alphabetical Opposites
Drills for Skills III
Student Blank Work Sheet

Your alphabetical ability will be tested as you try to think of five-letter words that are the opposites of the clues. Complete the clues on this sheet. Hide your answers. Then exchange your work sheet with a friend's. See who gets the most correct answers.

Clue	Opposite	Points
Example: asleep	A W A K E	10
1. _____	B _ _ _ _	_____
2. _____	C _ _ _ _	_____
3. _____	D _ _ _ _	_____
4. _____	E _ _ _ _	_____
5. _____	F _ _ _ _	_____
6. _____	G _ _ _ _	_____
7. _____	H _ _ _ _	_____
8. _____	I _ _ _ _	_____
9. _____	J _ _ _ _	_____
10. _____	K _ _ _ _	_____
11. _____	L _ _ _ _	_____
12. _____	M _ _ _ _	_____
13. _____	N _ _ _ _	_____
14. _____	O _ _ _ _	_____
15. _____	P _ _ _ _	_____
16. _____	Q _ _ _ _	_____
17. _____	R _ _ _ _	_____
18. _____	S _ _ _ _	_____
19. _____	T _ _ _ _	_____
20. _____	U _ _ _ _	_____
21. _____	V _ _ _ _	_____
22. _____	W _ _ _ _	_____
23. _____	X _ _ _ _	_____
24. _____	Y _ _ _ _	_____
25. slows	Z O O M S	1

Score total _____

Score ten points for each clue and answer that starts with the same letter. Score one point for all other answers. Total your score on the line provided.

Compound Word Connect-a-Dot
Drills for Skills IV

One of the oldest and easiest-to-play children's games is called Connect-a-Dot. Dots in square order are placed on a gameboard. Players alternate turns and connect two dots (horizontally/vertically only) anywhere on the board. The object is to be the player that completes the last side of a square. It is a great thinking game. You do not want to finish the third side of a square on your turn. If you do, your opponent will draw the fourth side, complete the square and put his initials in the square to show what he won. Compound Word Connect-a-Dot uses the same rules. This time, however, when you capture a box you capture the word in it for your word bank. When the game is completed, you take the captured words in your word bank and try to make as many compound words as you can. The player with the most compound words wins. Teacher Hint: I have this game in ten different versions. For math, each box contains a number. Whoever has the greatest total at the end of the game wins. For social studies, states and capitals are used. For English, synonyms, antonyms and homonyms are used. Compound words and word pieces are included in this book. There is a blank page for you to create your own challenges.

WORK	TO	SIDE	PLAY	HOUSE
SCHOOL	BODY	BOAT	LOOK	OUT
EVERY	ONE	DAY	BOOK	NIGHT
LIGHT	IN	YARD	GROUND	TIME
BOARD	UP	OVER	COME	SET

Player One's Bank	Player Two's Bank

Place your compound words on the back of this page.

GA1430

Word Construction Connect-a-Dot
Drills for Skills V

One of the oldest and easiest-to-play children's games is called Connect-a-Dot. Dots in square order are placed on a gameboard. Players alternate turns and connect two dots (horizontally/vertically only) anywhere on the board. The object is to be the player that completes the last side of a square. It is a great thinking game. You do not want to finish the third side of a square on your turn. If you do, your opponent will draw the fourth side, complete the square and put his initials in the square to show what he won. Word Construction Connect-a-Dot uses the same rules. This time, however, when you capture a box you capture the word piece in it for your word bank. When the game is completed, you take the captured word pieces in your word bank and try to make as many whole words as you can. The player with the most words wins. Each word must contain two captured pieces. Teacher Hint: I have this game in ten different versions. For math, each box contains a problem or answer. Whoever matches up the most problems in his bank at the end of the game wins. For social studies, famous people's first and last names are used. For English, words and their plural endings are spread over the board. Compound words and word pieces are included in this book. There is a blank master page for you to create your own challenges.

PL	B	ATE	AP	ST
OWN	INE	CL	R	UM
S	AY	AN	OUT	ON
AND	ORE	AIN	EAR	M
ALL	T	P	UG	ILL

Player One's Bank	Player Two's Bank

Place your compound words on the back of this page.

89

Connect-a-Dot
Drills for Skills VI
Blank Student Master

One of the oldest and easiest-to-play children's games is called Connect-a-Dot. Dots in square order are placed on a gameboard. Players alternate turns and connect two dots (horizontally/vertically only) anywhere on the board. The object is to be the player that completes the last side of a square. It is a great thinking game. You do not want to finish the third side of a square on your turn. If you do, your opponent will draw the fourth side, complete the square and put his initials in the square to show what he won. Use these same rules to create a game of your own. This time, when a player captures a box, he captures _____ in it for the bank. When the game is completed, he takes the captured _____ and places them in the bank and tries to make _____ as he can. The player with the most _____ wins.

Player One's Bank	Player Two's Bank

Use the back of this page for your answers.

GA1430

Upside-Down Drawing/Animal Studies
Ideas and Illustrations

The book *Drawing on the Right Side of Your Brain* has something in common with Maurice Sendak's *Pierre*. Both seem to encourage doing things upside down. In the case of Pierre it involves standing on your head. In *Drawing on the Right Side of the Brain* you are asked to draw objects upside down. Both of these techniques will be employed in the next challenge. Remember this challenge is for professional head standers only. This should not be done at home unless you have strict parental supervision. You will pick three objects to draw. I suggest an apple, a bottle and a face. You can pick three other ideas if you wish. Place each one in front of you and in the first column try to draw them the way they would look upside down. Then get a soft pillow, do a headstand and in the second column, while upside down, draw each object the way it would look right-side up. Note: If a wall is supporting your headstand, make sure you are in stocking feet.

Upside Down	Standing on Head
Apple	
Bottle	
Face	

 # Researching Helpful Organizations
Short-Term Project

The first thing that I thought about when I heard that Pierre didn't care was that this child needs some kind of help. There are many agencies throughout the world that help children with problems similar to Pierre's, as well as problems that are quite different from his. Years ago an agency called C.A.R.E. helped people in need of food and shelter all over the world. There are many local groups that also help. See what information you can find out about each of these groups and then draw a little sketch or cut out pictures and articles showing the type of work each group does.

Group/Description	Mini Drawing
Police Athletic League (PAL) _____ _____ _____	
Big Brother/Big Sister _____ _____ _____	
Last Wish Foundation _____ _____ _____	
Ronald McDonald House _____ _____ _____	
St. Jude's Hospital _____ _____ _____	

Can you think of any local groups that should be added to this list? Use the back of this paper to describe and illustrate the work of five other groups that help children and their families.

Student Suggestions

1. After researching philatelists, stamp issues and stamp values, design a commemorative stamp dedicated to Maurice Sendak and four of his stories. Design a bulletin board display for student-created stamps in all areas from literature to history to sports.

2. Design an "I Care" T-shirt highlighting the things you think are the most important "care" issues.

3. Design an "I Care" bumper sticker.

4. Research the making of maple syrup. On your next trip to the supermarket record the different manufacturers of pancake syrup. Survey the kids in the class to see what brands they use.

5. There are some cute little signs that people put on their lawns like "Chipmunk Crossing." Design a sign that uses lion information in it.

6. Cut out pictures of chairs from all sorts of books and magazines. After looking at a variety of features, design a chair that you can sit in backwards or forwards.

7. I think the author was joking when he said, "lovely cream of wheat." Make an illustrated chart of foods that you think would be "lovely." Liver and peas are on my "lovely" list.

8. Research who invented the chair and who invented some of the various models that we use today. See if your local car dealer can get you car seat testing information. *Consumer Report* has articles on children's car seats, and recliner chairs and other types of furniture.

9. Make a lion clock or watch that children would enjoy wearing or using in their houses or rooms.

10. Research theatrical and clown makeup. How has it changed over the years? If you are old enough, *FX 1* and *FX 2* at your video store are about a special effects artist. Write to Universal or MGM studios' theme parks for special effects information.

11. What other children's stories can you research that have morals? Make an illustrated poster of three morals. Look before you leap–show a blindfolded man or a man looking in the opposite direction crashing into a wall.

12. After studying the type of quilt designs and the organization of a quilting bee, make a quilt like the one on Pierre's bed. Get one swatch idea from each class member.

GA1430

Teacher Suggestions

1. Show the movie *The Mouse and the Motorcycle*. Compare the mouse's ride on Keith's motorcycle to Pierre's ride on the lion's back. Discuss the similarities and the differences in the two stories.

2. Have the children design a merry-go-round that animals might ride. On this ride the animals will be sitting on people and human-related ideas. Discuss with your class the ride parts that an animal might select.

3. Take a survey with your class on animals, other than horses, that children would like to ride on a merry-go-round. Have your class make models for homework.

4. Pierre was taken to the doctor for his "I don't care" problems. Research the types of doctors that children might visit for medical problems. Then discuss the types of ailments young children most often go to the doctor to remedy. Have the children record and illustrate the three most common maladies and then three out-of-the-ordinary visit reasons. Your less common visit illustrations will hopefully be as comical as my students' illustrations were.

5. Develop the idea with your class that furniture rental is a big business. It ranges from tables and chairs for conventions and weddings to complete setups for every room of your house. Have your children predict what types of things would be in the furniture rental top ten. Then have them investigate the costs of renting these items at three different rental agencies. Our survey showed that tables, chairs and televisions were one, two and three. The class can be split in four groups. One group can survey libraries for their top ten books taken out by children or adults. Another group can do video rental research, and a third group can check car leasing. Where do you think Pierre's folding chair was purchased or rented in our community?

6. Have the class make an illustrated checklist of the five things they would do if a friend was mistakenly eaten by a friendly lion.

7. Write five headlines for the Pierre story like "Lion Swallows Child." Using the theme in the given headline, design interview questions for the characters in this story. Then have your class act as reporters for different sections of the newspaper. They are to interview each character for the sports page, front page and the community page sections. Discuss with your students the differences in the way each of these articles should be written.

8. Have your class write dialogue for a scene where a lion is taken to the local veterinarian to get Pierre out of his stomach. Please remind them not to hurt the lion.

94

GA1430

Write Like a Master

Pierre was eaten but quickly removed from the lion's stomach. The story starter themes below involve food and being eaten by an animal. Try to add spicy words to your stories. Develop in the reader of your story a "caring" for the characters that you will place in your story. Design some story starters of your own that you can give to a friend, or ask your teacher to use your best ones with your classmates.

Story Starter or Oral Speaking Starter I

Jonah, no one is going to believe we were trapped in a whale's stomach unless we get out! Let's light a fire and see if we can make the whale sneeze us out. If that doesn't work, we can _____

_____

_____

Story Starter II

Nice bear! (shaking and said with great fear) Here is your cub back. I know one of the laws of the forest is never get between a bear and its cubs. I just wasn't thinking when I _____

_____

_____

Story Starter III

The circus is the greatest show on Earth. That lion tamer is the most fearless woman on Earth. She put her head right in that ferocious lion's mouth. One hiccup from that lion and ugh, I can't talk about it. Can you imagine her in school telling what she wants to be when she grows up? A lion tamer who not only _____

_____

but who is known for _____

_____

Story Starter IV

This is my last Bigfoot expedition. I'm starting to doubt my own findings. All my records show that_____

_____

Story Starter V

Pierre rode a lion. My big dream is one where I am riding a dinosaur. The dinosaur is a _____, so I'm not in any danger. We could be attacked by _____.

Gameboard

Materials Needed: Two number cubes, movers, light-colored crayons; Vexing Vocabulary; Just the Facts. Student-made and teacher-made question cards can be placed in the areas provided for them on the gameboard. They are optional but highly recommended. A card is picked each time a player has a multiple of five points in his/her bank (5, 10, 15, 20 or 25).

Players Needed: Two to four players or teams of two players

Play Procedures: Players alternate turns; throw number cubes; move in either direction at any time. This allows for playing strategies, rather than just mindlessly moving around a gameboard.

The Roll: Roll both number cubes. Your teacher will tell you to conduct some math operations with the number cubes. The three rules used most often in my classroom are

(a) Subtract the smaller from the larger; then move that many spaces (6 - 4 = <u>2</u>). Move two spaces.

(b) Multiply the two cubes and move the number of spaces in the one's column of the answer (2 x 6 = 1<u>2</u>). Move two spaces.

(c) Keep on adding the two cubes until you get one digit as the answer (6 + 6 = 12, 12 = 1 + 2 = 3). Move three spaces. Mathematicians call this finding the digital root.

Object: To score twenty-five points or to capture four won'ts, doctors, lions or people standing on their heads. Owning won'ts, doctors, lions or people standing on their heads can be accomplished by landing on them in a normal turn, trading for them when you land on a trading post or buying one of them for two times their value when you land on the bank. Each time you land on a property you color in (or initial) the little block in the corner of the property and put the points in your running bank. Ownership will change after trades only. Cross them out on the score sheet and add them to the other column. A scoreboard is provided for you. Each time someone lands on your property, he must pay you the number of points indicated in the top right-hand corner. Each time you land on your own property, you receive twice the points shown.

Winning Sets: Won'ts (eat, sleep, go to town and stand); doctors (one, two, three and four); lions (tiny, big, bigger and biggest); headstands (A, B, C and D)

Player One's Properties/Score	Player Two's Properties/Score

Game Card Property Pieces

On this page are the sixteen game pieces for *Pierre*. Cut them out and place them on oaktag to prolong their usability. Place a little box next to the gameboard as a storage area. Each time someone lands on an appropriate board space, he receives points and one of the game cards to verify property ownership. It also makes property trading much easier. The next time you play the game, design your own game card property pieces. Design a gameboard and create your own educational board game. Pick a theme. Then try to add important facts and intellectual flavor to your game.

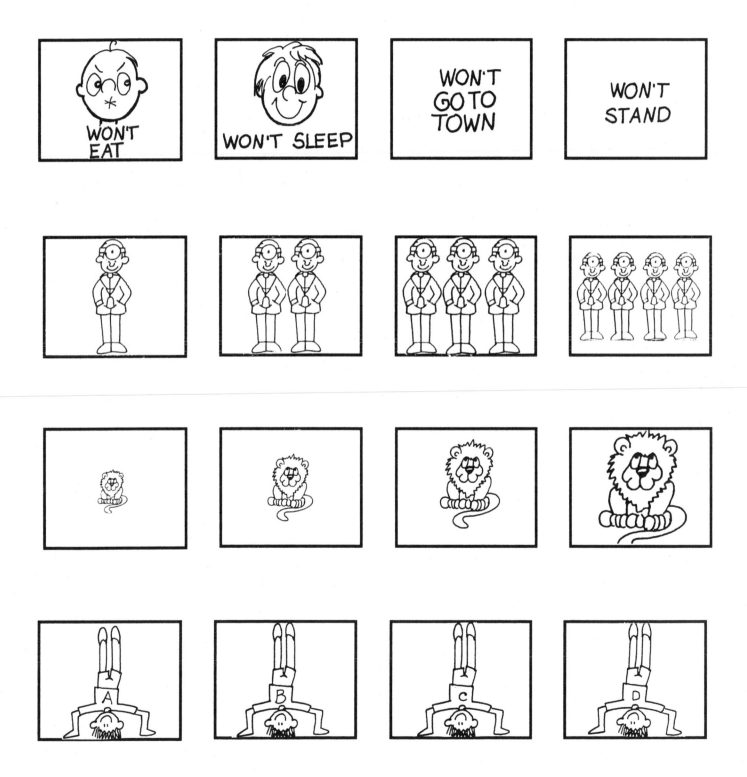

97

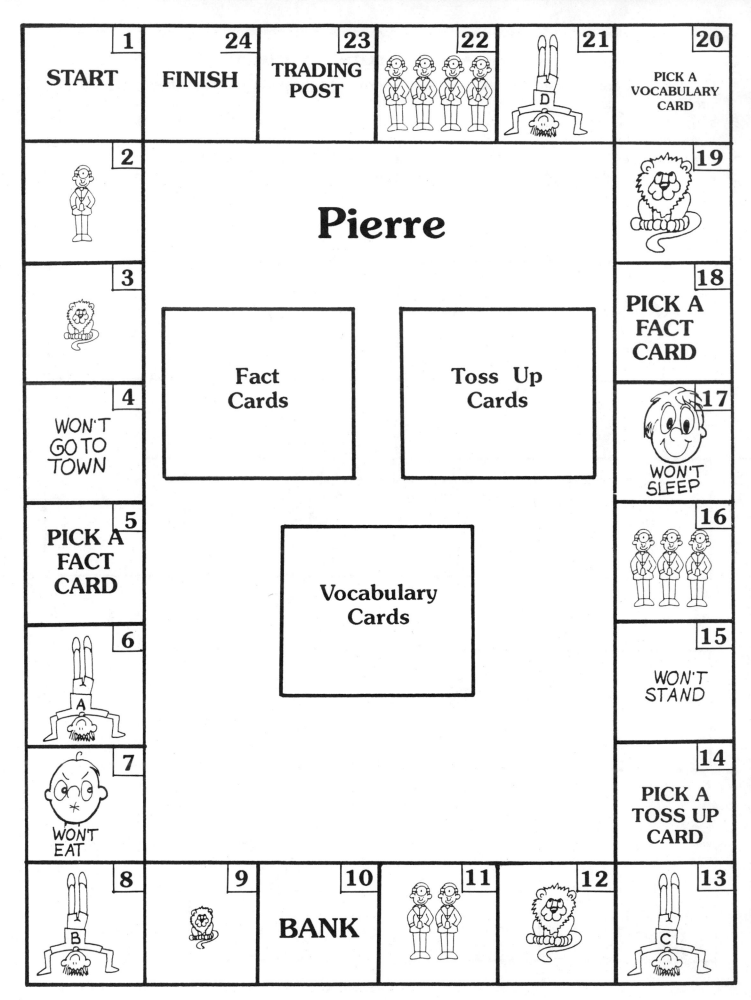

Dear Mili

Sharing

Aging

Grimm Fairy Tales

Caring Man

Carring Man

Rosebud

Carrying Mother

Unknown Forest   Identical Twins

Lead-Ins to Literature

Have you ever thought about how amazing sleep is? One second you are tired and the next morning, presto! Ready to go full steam ahead. Have you ever thought of the Rip Van Winkle Syndrome? One second you are asleep and the next morning, presto! Thirty years later. Have you ever thought . . . enough of this thinking! Let's get on with the story. A mother protects her daughter from war by sending her deep into the woods. She is there for what she thinks is three days. In reality, thirty years have passed. She is the same little girl, but the world isn't the same. She is on her way back to her mother's house when. . . . This is a lead-in and I am certainly not going to ruin this book for you by telling you everything. Maybe you'll get lucky and your teacher will read this book to your class.

1. Don't you hate it when someone uses trickery to try to get you to read a good story? You do? You don't? Explain. _____
_____

2. If you were in the deep forest, is there any way that you would be able to tell that thirty years have passed, not three days? Remember the girl's body has not changed in any way after each night's sleep. _____
_____

3. In addition to war, what three reasons would cause you to send your child deep into the woods without an escort?

   a. _____

   b. _____

   c. _____

4. How do you think the child felt being left alone in the forest? _____
_____

5. At first the girl feels abandoned. Then she feels that her guardian angel is watching over her. Why do you think this would rid her of all her fears?_____
_____

6. What situations would you confront this girl with in the forest? Think of at least two good happenings and two potential dangers that she might encounter. _____
_____

7. In what country would you place this story? Why?_____
_____

100

GA1430

Just the Facts

1. What type of flower did the man hand the little girl?_____

2. What was the girl talking about when she mentioned the nails that were on heaven's door?

   _____

3. Three things told the mother that war was approaching very quickly. What were they?

   a._____

   b._____

   c._____

4. What was placed in the child's pocket before she was sent into the woods? _____

5. What did the woodpeckers, hawks and crows do?_____

6. Who showed the little girl the way through the forest? _____

7. The little girl's dress was grabbed by what she thought were wild beasts. They were really

   _____ that took hold of the material.

8. What three things made up the first meal at the old man's house?

   a._____

   b._____

   c._____

9. The little girl suggested that she sleep on _____, but the old man gave her his

   _____ instead.

10. The two little girls could have been identical twins except for the difference in their _____.

11. Binweed is a white cup-shaped _____.

12. The mother thought that _____ had torn her daughter to pieces.

13. What was the old woman enjoying when the young child first saw her? _____

14. It was only natural that when the child returned to her village thirty years later that the village would look _____ and _____ to her.

15. Where was the blooming rose found? _____

What Is Your Opinion?

1. How hard do you think it was for a mother to just cast her daughter into unknown woods? Explain._____
_____

2. What other things might the mother have done to protect her child from the dangers of war? Can you think of three other options? _____
   a. _____
   b. _____
   c. _____

3. The young girl in the story met a playmate in the woods. Why do you think the child met what appeared to be her twin?
_____
_____

4. Do you think the color of the rose was important to the meaning of the story?
_____
_____

5. The little girl gave the old man more than half of the food that she had prepared. Why did the author put this fact into the story?
_____
_____

6. If a complete stranger told you he knew you were coming, wouldn't you ask him a lot of questions about how this could be possible?
_____
_____

7. Should guardian angels be invisible in stories, or would it be more interesting if everyone could see your guardian angel?
_____
_____

8. I don't understand the ending to *Dear Mili*. Do you feel the child should have died with her mother? How would you explain the strange ending?
_____
_____

9. Red wine shouldn't be used to give a child energy, but at the time it was given to the little girl, she was really forty years old. Do you agree about the forty years, and do you think wine should be given to children or adults for energy? Explain.
_____
_____

10. Where would you have added additional characters to the story to make it more interesting?
_____
_____

Last Is First Sentences
Vexing Vocabulary

violets
venerable
glimpse
chasm
tumult
fir
idle
meadows

obedient
splendid
neighbors
furiously
overran
suddenly
angel
rosebud

moss
amazement
fleecy
buffeted
mercy
gloriously
scraped
faint

Super Challenge

1. Combine five spelling words in a "last is first" sentence. This means that the last letter in each word that you use must be used to begin the next word in the sentence. Somewhere in the sentence you must insert one of the vocabulary words at the top.
   Example: The elephant took Ken's sweets *suddenly*.

   a. _____

   b. _____

   c. _____

   d. _____

   e. _____

Semi-Super Challenge

2. Combine five spelling words in an "every beginning letter is the same" sentence. This means that the first letter you use in each word must be the same. You must, also, insert one spelling word in each of your sentences.
   Example: Frank Fisher first felt *faint* Friday.

   a. _____

   b. _____

   c. _____

   d. _____

   e. _____

Easy Challenge

3. Pick five of your favorite singers and design a song title that uses one of the vocabulary words at the top and starts with the first letter of the singer's last name.
   Example: Amy Grant–"*Glimpses* of a Past Love"
            Elvis Presley–"Pretty *Angel*"

   a. _____

   b. _____

   c. _____

   d. _____

   e. _____

GA1430

Mil Words
Drills for Skills

Each clue below will help you find a word that has *mil* in it. After finding the correct *mil* word, place a word that will rhyme with it on the next blank.

Clue	Answer	Rhyming Word
Example: boy's name	Milt	tilt
1. large number		billion
2. driving distance		pile
3. the army		
4. face feature		
5. girl's name		
6. calm manner		
7. much needed drink		
8. a fungus		
9. large building		
10. our galaxy		
11. roadside marker		
12. centipede kin		
13. time unit		
14. Wisconsin City		
15. hat maker		
16. famous poet		
17. a plant		

Take the *dea* in *dear* just like we took the *mil* in *Mili* and write five clues for words that your classmates can try to guess.

1. _____
2. _____
3. _____
4. _____
5. _____

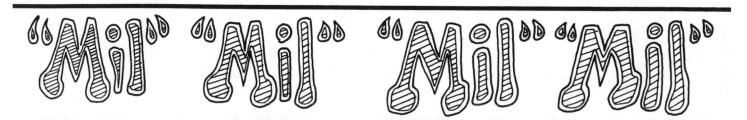

You Are Art
Ideas and Illustrations

Get a large piece of art paper and divide it into four parts. Twenty-five "You Are" themes are listed below. Pick four of them to illustrate, one in each section. Some children may choose to do a larger mural with a "you are" label on each drawing. Think of a situation that will occur if each "you are" theme was put into practice or actually happened to you. Develop each template into a mini story with accompanying illustrations.

1. You are an identical triplet.

2. You are a chocolate freak.

3. You are a fashion or food designer.

4. You are a designer of creative devices for children who are hearing impaired.

5. You are thirty years old, but your body has not changed since age ten.

6. You are twelve but you have a Rip Van Winkle beard or hair longer than Rapunzel's tresses.

7. You are the creator of talking appliances.

8. You are the person that is shot out of a cannon. You are known as "Hardheaded _____ (your name)."

9. You are the seller of machines to mad scientists.

10. You are Father Time, the control of everyone's time.

11. You are the tin soldier in Hans Christian Andersen's famous tale.

12. You are a food fight referee.

13. You are an electronic bowling ball.

14. You are a "baseball hat wearing" ballet dancer.

15. You are the driver in a demolition derby.

16. You are the world's record holder for holding your breath underwater.

17. You have just participated in a quantum leap. Show the first scene, then the new scene that you were thrust into.

18. You are trapped in a cave full of bats.

19. You are a storytelling coin from the past.

20. You are a victim innocently jailed.

21. You are a scarecrow.

22. You are lost in a maze.

23. You are the discoverer of Atlantis, the Lost Underwater City.

24. You are being chased by the headless horseman.

25. You are the little girl's mother in *Dear Mili.*

GA1430

Short-Term Project

Dear Mili was a recently discovered work of Jakob and Wilhelm Grimm. Their interest in language and folklore led them to create a large body of works that can be appreciated by young children as well as college professors. See what ideas you can find in each topic area below before designing a new Grimm tale to add to their fairy tale works.

Topics

Hansel/Gretel _____
_____

Rumpelstiltskin _____
_____

Children and family tales _____
_____

Goose Girl _____
_____

University of Gottingen _____
_____

Living together throughout their lives, even though Wilhelm was married _____
_____

Their history of the German language _____
_____

Their birthplace–Hanau, Hesse-Cassel _____
_____

Your Fairy Tale (flip this paper/please expand your ideas)

Name of fairy tale: _____
Character's problem: _____
Importance of setting: _____
Description of ending: _____

106

Student Suggestions

1. What can you find out about the various classifications of roses? Illustrate five different types of roses. Read about the history of the flower trade from the Netherlands. Make a mini chart tracing from when the flower is first cut to when it arrives at your local store for purchase. Flower orders are bid upon just like a horse auction. See what you can find out about this process.

2. Flower growing is a gigantic business. See what you can find out about this country's and the world's leading flower growers. Who is number one in flower exports and imports? How much is spent on flower purchases in the United States each year?

3. Get catalogs from the three leading senders of flowers and flowergrams. Compare their prices, and then design a flower-sending catalog of your own. Put some of your own invented flowers and their descriptions next to your drawing of real flowers that your service delivers. Design a logo and a delivery truck for your new company.

4. Research the world's greatest forests. Where would you place the Brazilian rain forests and the Black Forest of Germany on your rating list?

5. Create a song or poem that will salute the Grimm brothers' contributions to children's literature.

6. Design a Helpful Hints to Flower Care poster that would be on display at a local flower shop.

7. Create a handy wallet-sized paper with ten hints for little children lost in the woods. Make five of your suggestions humorous and five serious. Place three illustrations around your helpful hints booklets.

8. Make a You Should Never Go in the Woods Because paper. List five humorous things that might happen to you in the woods.

9. Start a campaign to end all wars. Find out what local organizations can help you with your research and campaign.

10. Discuss three reasons why you think *Dear Mili* will make a good movie or animated feature.

11. You are a lawyer defending the mother in *Dear Mili* for casting her child into the woods. Describe how you would defend her.

12. Change the scene in the story from a forest to a desert. Describe how the story would change.

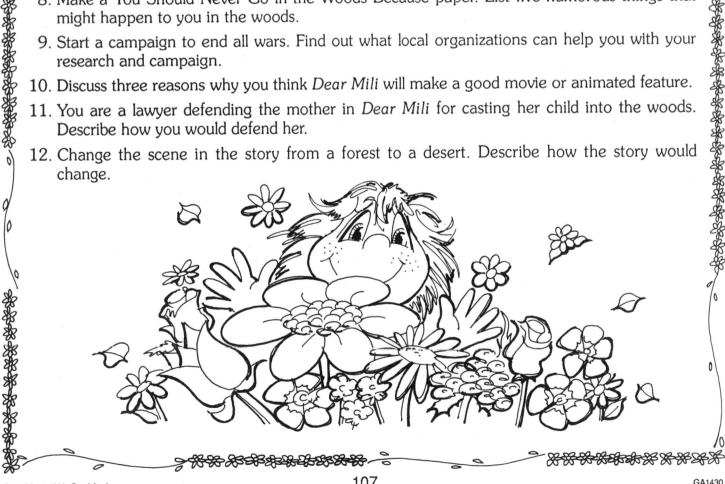

Teacher Suggestions

1. The crisis of war and having to send a child into the woods alone is a serious one. Discuss with your class what other serious situations authors put young children into to increase the attention of young readers. See if they can name some of the situations that they liked best and some that they liked least.

2. Have your class design a fairy tale theme park stressing the fairy tales of Wilhelm and Jakob Grimm. Have them create a roller coaster that will tour some of the features of the park. Create a list of most desired jobs that children would like to have at a theme park. Research the five best theme parks in the country and plan an imaginary trip to each one. Have your students compare the prices and features of MGM and Universal Studios theme parks to determine which is the better value.

3. Have your class enlarge their favorite flowers using the overhead projector. Then have them research the flower's various varieties. This makes a *Honey I Shrunk the Kids* looking hallway with great flower information.

4. Have your class research Wise Decisions in Children's Literature. Make a list and then illustrate other wise decisions that appear in children's stories, like the mother sending her daughter into the woods to protect her from war.

5. Have your class design lunch box covers that salute Grimms' fairy tales.

6. Discuss commemorative stamps and plates with your class. Then take paper plates and design *Dear Mili* commemorative plates. This works just as well in a history unit where you are designing historical plates commemorating an event in history, science where you are doing famous scientists, or athletics where you are chronicling world records or your favorite sports team.

7. Draw a map of Dear Mili's forest. Place additional locations on the map like roadside rests, overnight lodging, rosebud waterfall and additional sites not talked about in the book.

8. Have your class design a notebook of headlines that would relate to *Dear Mili*–Young Girl Missing in Forest, Flowers Stolen from Joseph's Garden, War Is Imminent.

9. Giving someone more than half of a scarce portion of food is a sign of a thoughtful person. Make a Things Thoughtful People Do illustrated/topical mural with your class.

Write Like a Master

Each of your stories is centered around the mystery of a thick forest. Try to sprinkle your writing with elves, sprites and magical ideas. Use some of the themes in *Dear Mili* in your writing. Think of some of Grimms' fairy tales and the pictures they tried to weave. See if you can get people to quickly care for the people in your stories.

Story Starter I

We have to part, my little precious. You'll be fine. Your mother is sending you into the woods with Fenwick. He will _____

_____

_____

Story Starter II

I am Rhodon, the king of the forest. I may be small, but I am powerful. Nothing happens in these woods without my permission. You have entered my domain without my approval. The consequences are _____

_____

_____

Story Starter III

The life of a wood nymph is one of mystery and joy. I_____

_____

_____

Story Starter IV

No one ever likes the witch in a children's story. I guess they never stop to consider her feelings. She is always lonely because _____

_____

_____

Story Starter V

If you leave the top off the bottle, I can come and go as I please. I promise you I won't escape and that each of your wishes will be granted. You can trust me because _____

_____

_____

GA1430

Gameboard

Materials Needed: Two number cubes, movers, light-colored crayons; Vexing Vocabulary; Just the Facts. Student-made and teacher-made question cards can be placed in the areas provided for them on the gameboard. They are optional but highly recommended. A card is picked each time a player has a multiple of five points in his/her bank (5, 10, 15, 20 or 25).

Players Needed: Two to four players or teams of two players

Play Procedures: Players alternate turns; throw number cubes; move in either direction at any time. This allows for playing strategies, rather than just mindlessly moving around a gameboard.

The Roll: Roll both number cubes. Your teacher will tell you to conduct some math operations with the number cubes. The three rules used most often in my classroom are

    (a) Subtract the smaller from the larger; then move that many spaces (6 - 4 = <u>2</u>). Move two spaces.

    (b) Multiply the two cubes and move the number of spaces in the one's column of the answer (2 x 6 = 1<u>2</u>). Move two spaces.

    (c) Keep on adding the two cubes until you get one digit as the answer (6 + 6 = 12, 12 = 1 + 2 = 3). Move three spaces. Mathematicians call this finding the digital root.

Object: To score twenty-five points or to capture four cabins, wise people, flowers or salutations. Owning cabins, wise people, flowers or salutations can be accomplished by landing on them in a normal turn, trading for them when you land on a trading post or buying one of them for two times their value when you land on the bank. Each time you land on a property you color in (or initial) the little block in the corner of the property and put the points in your running bank. Ownership will change after trades only. Cross them out on the score sheet and add them to the other column. A scoreboard is provided for you. Each time someone lands on your property, he must pay you the number of points indicated in the top right-hand corner. Each time you land on your own property, you receive twice the points shown.

Winning Sets: Cabins (one, two, three and four); wise people (sage, oracle, soothsayer, Joseph); flowers (rose, carnation, tulip, daisy); partings (farewell, so long, good-bye, see you)

Player One's Properties/Score	Player Two's Properties/Score

Game Card Property Pieces

On this page are the sixteen pieces for *Dear Mili*. Cut them out and place them on oaktag to prolong their usability. Place a little box next to the gameboard as a storage area. Each time someone lands on an appropriate board space, he receives points and one of the game cards to verify property ownership. It also makes property trading much easier. The next time you play the game, design your own game card property pieces. Design a gameboard and create your own educational board game. Pick a theme. Then try to add important facts and intellectual flavor to your game.

Dear Mili

112

Seven Questions Pride

Kenny's Window

Rooster Riddles

Teddy Bear Talk

Window Wonders

Halfway There

Room for a Friend Dream Objects

113

Lead-Ins to Literature

How would you explain your strangest dream to a friend? Would you tell the friend that you received a seven-part mission while you were asleep? Would you tell this friend that the seven parts of your mission were written down on a piece of paper in your pocket when you awoke from this dream? Probably not! It just sounds too unbelievable, especially carrying something written out of a dream. Kenny swears it is true. Maybe reading *Kenny's Dream* will bring you a little closer to your dreams and what they mean.

1. Try to explain three ways that writing could be carried out of a dream. _____

_____

2. If you were given seven questions in a dream, would you go out and try to find their answers? In what situations would you/wouldn't you find the answers? _____

_____

3. What three problems that a dream gives you would you like to solve?

    a. _____

    b. _____

    c. _____

4. Do you have any objects that appear in more than one of your dreams? Why do you think they appear? Are these objects something you enjoy or the opposite? _____

_____

5. What was the funniest part of a recent dream? _____

_____

6. If you were able to fashion your dreams before you went to sleep, what character would you like to have appear in your dream in each of the categories below?

    a singer_____

    a cartoon character_____

    one of Snow White's dwarfs _____

    a wicked storybook character _____

    a character that would make a good friend_____

Use the space below to draw a dream machine. Label each part of your machine with specific directions.

GA1430

Just the Facts

1. What is half way to wherever you want to go? _____

2. In what part of the train was the rooster riding? _____

3. Who was Kenny's oldest and best friend? _____

4. *Scare* rhymed with what word in Kenny's first attempt at poetry? _____

5. David was Kenny's _____ friend.

6. Where did Kenny go to find "an only goat"? _____

7. Bucky's eye was made out of _____.

8. What was the last gift that Kenny gave to the goat that was supposed to be an only goat?

   _____

9. The snow ran down the window in long sad drips. This made Kenny think that the window

   was _____.

10. Baby pretended to be an _____.

11. Kenny picked a wide variety of flowers on his trip down the mountain. What colors were

    they? _____

12. Where were the seven questions hidden? _____

13. Who could never get lost? _____

14. Who doesn't have to pay the fare on a bus? _____

15. Kenny loved the goat better than what three things? _____

    _____

16. Where did the words *coming home your only boy Kenny* appear? _____

17. What did Kenny bang his fist on that made the whole bed jump? _____

18. The man kissed what part of the baby's body? _____

19. Why did Kenny's ship need an extra room? _____

20. Kenny put the complaining soldier on the window ledge. What stopped the soldier from tap-

    ping on the glass when he was cold? _____

What Is Your Opinion?

1. Did the author make it believable that a person could come out of a dream with real objects and a real mission? Explain your answer. _____

   _____

   _____

2. A rooster seemed like a strange animal to choose for the part of a wise creature. Would you have picked an owl to report to? Do you think the author picked the rooster because it is rarely used as the symbol for wisdom in children's stories?_____

   _____

   _____

3. Which question was the most challenging for Kenny? Why? _____

   _____

4. Do you think dreams should be thrown away just because they seem like they may be impossible to reach? _____

   _____

5. What did you like best about Bucky the teddy bear? Would you want a talking teddy bear?

   _____

   _____

   _____

6. How did you feel about the way Kenny treated the toy soldier? Could some other method have been used? _____

   _____

7. What are the good and bad points of living in a garden that is half day and half night? List three of each.

   _____

   _____

   _____

8. Do you think Kenny was a lonely boy? Why do you think he kept asking for a room for a friend? Doesn't this sound like he really needed a friend? _____

   _____

9. How many times have promises been broken to you? What do you feel like when this happens? Can you understand that sometimes promises have to be broken, or do you think they never should be broken? _____

   _____

   _____

10. Why do you think Kenny would be a good friend for you? _____

   _____

Kenny's Window

Vexing Vocabulary

soldier	bouquet	whirled
angrily	shivered	extra
Switzerland	lead	pajama
nighttime	rooster	chalk
shiny	snowflake	checkerboard
beckoning	lonely	escape
eagerly	feathers	asleep
thumped	garden	question

Hi, Sport Fans,
   How about trying some famous people letter writing with the twenty-four vocabulary words above.

Thanks for your attention to your vocabulary,
Mickey Mantle

Write a short note using five of the vocabulary words above. The note must reflect some part of each famous person's job or personality.

Don Mattingly (baseball) _____

_____

_____

Paula Abdul (music) _____

_____

_____

Oprah Winfrey (television)_____

_____

_____

The Roadrunner (cartoons)_____

_____

_____

Walt Disney (amusement parks) _____

_____

_____

On the back, pick three additional "short note characters" of your own and incorporate vocabulary words in their letters.

Alphabetical I.Q. (for super students only)
Drills for Skills I

Your alphabetical I.Q. will be tested as you try to find the opposite of each word presented in the left column. Your answer must contain six letters and as you can see the answers are in alphabetical order. Use the blank master on the following page and see if you can write the clues for each letter of the alphabet that will give you a synonym for each word.

Clues

1. question
2. margarine
3. opened
4. patient
5. cause
6. enemy
7. generous
8. weight
9. outside
10. sad
11. saved
12. ugly
13. ends
14. ignore
15. sheriff
16. execute
17. incites
18. place
19. eat
20. marksmen
21. straightens
22. guess
23. stupidity
24. photographs
25. whispered
26. button

Answers

A _ _ _ _ _ _
B _ _ _ _ _ _
C _ _ _ _ _ _
D _ _ _ _ _ _
E _ _ _ _ _ _
F _ _ _ _ _ _
G _ _ _ _ _ _
H _ _ _ _ _ _
I _ _ _ _ _ _
J _ _ _ _ _ _
K _ _ _ _ _ _
L _ _ _ _ _ _
M _ _ _ _ _ _
N _ _ _ _ _ _
O _ _ _ _ _ _
P _ _ _ _ _ _
Q _ _ _ _ _ _
R _ _ _ _ _ _
S _ _ _ _ _ _
T _ _ _ _ _ _
U _ _ _ _ _ _
V _ _ _ _ _ _
W _ _ _ _ _ _
X _ _ _ _ _ _
Y _ _ _ _ _ _
Z _ _ _ _ _ _

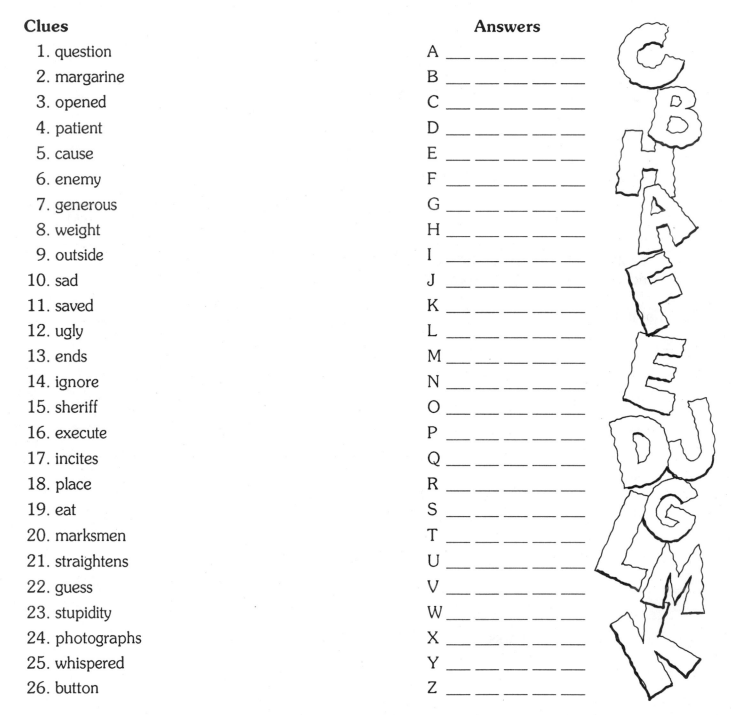

Make an alphabetical list of three, four or five-letter words that have obvious opposites. Exchange your list with a classmate. In a two-minute time period see who gets the most answers correct. Try this with synonyms, too.

118

Alphabetical I.Q. (for super students only)
Blank Master
Drills for Skills I

Your alphabetical I.Q. will be tested as you try to find the synonym of each word presented in the left column. Your answer must contain six letters and as you can see the answers are in alphabetical order. Use this page to generate three, four or five-letter words, also.

Clues

1. _____
2. _____
3. _____
4. _____
5. _____
6. _____
7. _____
8. _____
9. _____
10. _____
11. _____
12. _____
13. _____
14. _____
15. _____
16. _____
17. _____
18. _____
19. _____
20. _____
21. _____
22. _____
23. _____
24. _____
25. _____
26. _____

Answers

A __ __ __ __ __
B __ __ __ __ __
C __ __ __ __ __
D __ __ __ __ __
E __ __ __ __ __
F __ __ __ __ __
G __ __ __ __ __
H __ __ __ __ __
I __ __ __ __ __
J __ __ __ __ __
K __ __ __ __ __
L __ __ __ __ __
M __ __ __ __ __
N __ __ __ __ __
O __ __ __ __ __
P __ __ __ __ __
Q __ __ __ __ __
R __ __ __ __ __
S __ __ __ __ __
T __ __ __ __ __
U __ __ __ __ __
V __ __ __ __ __
W __ __ __ __ __
X __ __ __ __ __
Y __ __ __ __ __
Z __ __ __ __ __

Make an alphabetical list of three, four or five-letter words that have obvious opposites. Exchange your list with a classmate. In a two-minute time period see who gets the most answers correct. Try this with synonyms, too.

Skiing Words
Drills for Skills II

Three ski courses have been provided for you below. As you ski down the mountain, you are trying to find words whose letters are in consecutive order. As you go through each gate, grab a letter for the words you are constructing. Please do some warm-up activities before starting this word course. We don't want you to pull any mental muscles.

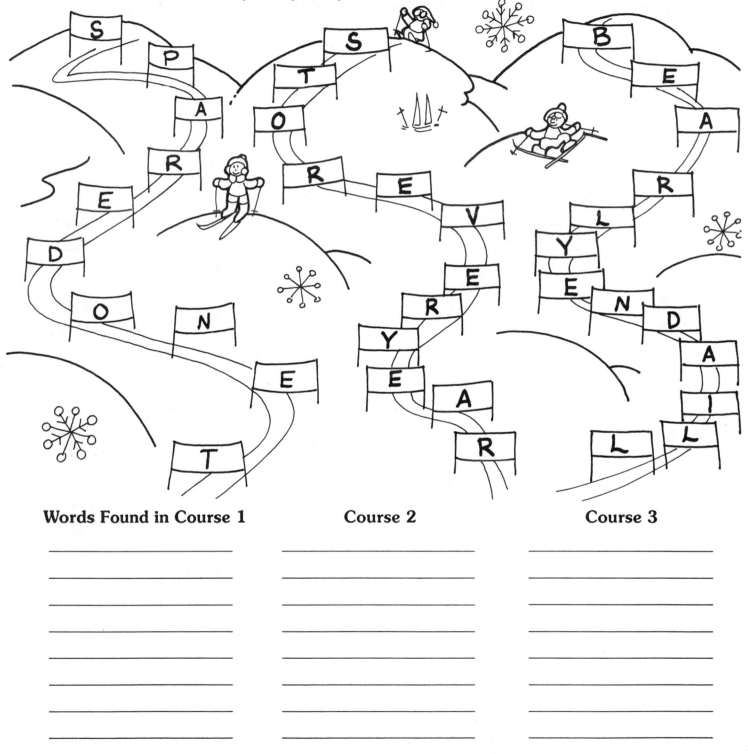

Words Found in Course 1

_____
_____
_____
_____
_____
_____
_____

Course 2

_____
_____
_____
_____
_____
_____
_____

Course 3

_____
_____
_____
_____
_____
_____
_____

Design three courses for a friend to ski.

120

GA1430

Alphabet and Number Concept Books
Ideas and Illustrations

You are about to become the author and illustrator of a book for young children. Your task is to create an original way to teach the ABC's by designing an alphabet book for young children. You have two weeks to complete this task. Thirteen of your letter creations will be handed in next week, and the remaining thirteen will be handed in the week after. Review *Alligators All Around, One Was Johnny, Chicken Soup with Rice, The Z Was Zapped*, and the hundreds of other ABC theme books that you can find at your local library and bookstore before starting this assignment. Some ideas handed in by my classes included

1. *Adam's Baseball Creations:* Each page was a famous player performing a task young children could understand. Alliteration was also used throughout the book. Hank Aaron ate the apples. Mickey Mantle moved Mom's mirror. Adam and his partner Josh tried to use Hall of Fame players wherever possible.

2. *Isa's Animals:* Each letter of the alphabet was an animal. Not creative, you say! He used his face and enhanced it to become a turtle, snake or elephant.

3. *Danny's Hulk Hogan's Homonyms:* He used various wrestlers to teach word meanings. I didn't realize there was a different wrestler for every letter of the alphabet.

4. *Kezia's Mariah Carey's Counting Book:* She took cutout pictures of this well-known singer and taught the numbers from one to ten with her additional illustrations.

5. *Ben's ABC's of Rocks* was stretching it a little bit, but why not see if you can put your favorite subject or a hobby into an ABC book.

6. *Sou Nun's Geography ABC's* had the outline of a state or country and what you could do there. The topics ran from Meet the Midshipmen in Maryland to Jump in Jamaica's Waters.

7. Rachel did flowers. She had drawn each flower as it was acting out the action word. Zinnias zooming was my favorite. She had two flowers sitting in a race car that was flying down the street. See if you can take the commonplace and put it into an "unthought of" situation like this.

8. Ten different people used the world of fashion; three used foods and drink; two used candy bars; horses, dogs and cats had one book each. Comic characters were represented, also.

121

GA1430

Short-Term Project

Children's Circle–Where Books Come Alive has a fantastic video on the Maurice Sendak library. It features six of his books and musical renditions by Carole King. It contains a segment called "Getting to Know Maurice Sendak."

In it Mr. Sendak discusses bits of his childhood, his book and his illustrations. Preview the tape because you are now responsible for performing the lead-ins to each of his books into rhyme form. No easy task for any writer! See what you can design for

Alligators All Around

_____

_____

Pierre

_____

_____

One Was Johnny

_____

_____

Chicken Soup with Rice

_____

_____

Where the Wild Things Are

_____

_____

In the Night Kitchen

_____

_____

Introducing Maurice Sendak

_____

_____

Introducing yourself in poem form

_____

_____

Introducing your best friend in poem form

_____

_____

_____

GA1430

Student Suggestions

1. How much would it cost to own and keep a horse where you live? Make a chart titled "City Horse, Country Horse" and research the difference in prices for lodging, feed, training and workout tracks. If you owned a racehorse, what would your schedule be the day of the race?

2. Highlight three games played at least one hundred years ago. Use a poster format to present your ideas or design the gameboards that were actually used. Make your directions easy to follow.

3. Make a list of "What looks inside, what looks outside." There are many obvious answers, but there are also answers that are imagination stretchers. Try to create both in your writing.

Inside	**Outside**
X rays	a window
love	faith
refrigerator	telescope

4. Make a sales catalog of everyday, famous and humorous beds. Include their description, prices and longevity records. Interview a furniture salesperson. Find out what is the most frequently selected bed style/material (wood, metal, formica) and some of the newer options available to bed shoppers. Create a *Ripley's Believe It or Not* book on beds–bed records: largest, smallest, fastest moving, easiest to make, lightest, most features, most expensive.

5. Research the effects of dreams on a person's health. Why don't we remember all our dreams? Can you program yourself to dream in a certain area? What can be done for young children who continually have bad dreams? What should young children be told about why they sometimes have bad dreams? Ask your family doctor to recommend a good book about dreams and dream research.

6. Write a scenario showing our present day world where all the humans as well as animals can talk. How would this change the way we live?

7. Write a mini essay on "What Is Pride?"

8. Design a poster titled "(your name goes here) the Pride of the (your last name goes here) Family." Make a humorous poster, telling that the truth might hurt too much.

9. Design an animal riding area for young children. Focus on the educational value of each animal you place in your animal riding theme park. Make your illustrations attractive.

10. Place two of your own research ideas for your class below.

_____

_____

123

GA1430

Teacher Suggestions

1. Start a "Letters to Mama or Papa" writing program. Discuss with your class five situations, like Kenny in *Kenny's Window*, that kids get into where they might want to write a letter home. Some camp topics might be poison ivy, poor food, night noises, outdoor bathrooms, cold showers, swimming test, parents' day, the skunk. "Letters to Home" topics might include Grandma's house, invitation to the science fair/ethnic food luncheon, class trip invite, sorry I broke your favorite dish, do I have to have a brother, can Jenny sleep over, I'm going to Joe's after school, I miss you. Refrigerator notes could also be written, using eight words and two pictures describing any situation. No smiley faces allowed on any part of your note, please. The funnier the item it is written on, the better.

2. Discuss with your class the importance of budgeting time for the tasks they have to do in the future. Make a time line that incorporates Kenny's tasks on it. Make a mini illustration above each task that Kenny pursued. Use this same technique on seven tasks the class does in a school day.

3. We had an excellent discussion on what would happen in your garden, house or school if it were night on one side and day on the other. This discussion was generated from the part of *Kenny's Window* where he wished for a garden that had the moon on one side and the sun on the other. Isaac Asimov would have been proud of our creative ideas.

4. Play What's My Line with your class. The contestant must either be a book or a character from a book. Research and questions and answers the contestant thinks will be asked of him/her are to be handed in before he appears on the show.

5. Research children's books and stories where a toy is central to the theme of the story. *The Tin Soldier*, *The Velveteen Rabbit*, *The Phantom Tollbooth*.

6. Pet Poetry: Following the theme of Kenny's poem to Bucky the bear, have your class compose poems to introduce characters from books they have read. We started with Donald Duck and Minnie Mouse and worked our way up to the Cyclops in *The Brave Little Tailor*.

7. Kenny's visit to the valleys in Switzerland provides an excellent stepping-stone to an educational visit to Switzerland. Have your class plan a ski trip or a mountain climbing expedition to Switzerland; then within the confines of your classroom take the trip.

8. Put a seven-part mural up of each child's illustrations of Kenny's seven missions. The story reminds me of the labors of Hercules. Upper grades can be introduced to Hercules' story and each labor before illustrating their favorite.

Write Like a Master

The theme for these story starters is the mystery of dreams. In your writing try to convince the reader that dreams are secret messages or waves of ideas from the future that the mind picks up while you are sleeping. Don't overdo your stories. Try to plant an idea that an imaginative reader just might believe.

Story Starter I

Have you ever brought an object out of one of your dreams? I'm not talking about a monster like you see in the movies. I'm talking about small things. Last week I dreamed about a music box. In the morning when I awoke, the little character that spins on top of the music box was in my hand. Two weeks ago there was a heart locket in my hand from a story an imaginary grandmother was telling me. Last night's dream was about Candyland. This morning my hand contained a Hershey's Kiss that was half caramel just like the dream. Each object only seems to last until a new one appears in my hand. This is probably a way that _____

_____

_____

Story Starter II

Everyone is talking about the wonderful work of Dreams Come True. It is an agency that grants the wishes of very ill children. The meaningful work they do is important to the children and their families. It helps_____

_____

_____

Story Starter III

Flashback is the newest idea from the Dreamtelic Corporation. If you had a particularly good dream, you can put the mega-helmet on and it will bring back your thoughts. It also allows you to see the dreams you can't remember in the morning. They are putting a new feature on next year's helmet that will allow you to _____

_____

_____

Story Starter IV

Dream Cat is my favorite cartoon character. I enjoy seeing him/her get out of funny situations. Yesterday the writer had him/her _____

_____

_____

GA1430

Gameboard

Materials Needed: Two number cubes, movers, light-colored crayons; Vexing Vocabulary; Just the Facts. Student-made and teacher-made question cards can be placed in the areas provided for them on the gameboard. They are optional but highly recommended. A card is picked each time a player has a multiple of five points in his/her bank (5, 10, 15, 20 or 25).

Players Needed: Two to four players or teams of two players

Play Procedures: Players alternate turns; throw number cubes; move in either direction at any time. This allows for playing strategies, rather than just mindlessly moving around a gameboard.

The Roll: Roll both number cubes. Your teacher will tell you to conduct some math operations with the number cubes. The three rules used most often in my classroom are

    (a) Subtract the smaller from the larger; then move that many spaces (6 - 4 = <u>2</u>). Move two spaces.

    (b) Multiply the two cubes and move the number of spaces in the one's column of the answer (2 x 6 = 1<u>2</u>). Move two spaces.

    (c) Keep on adding the two cubes until you get one digit as the answer (6 + 6 = 12, 12 = 1 + 2 = 3). Move three spaces. Mathematicians call this finding the digital root.

Object: To score twenty-five points or to capture four wise animals, toy soldiers, one-eyed teddy bears or look fors. Owning wise animals, toy soldiers, one-eyed teddy bears or look fors can be accomplished by landing on them in a normal turn, trading for them when you land on a trading post or buying one of them for two times their value when you land on the bank. Each time you land on a property you color in (or initial) the little block in the corner of the property and put the points in your running bank. Ownership will change after trades only. Cross them out on the score sheet and add them to the other column. A scoreboard is provided for you. Each time someone lands on your property, he must pay you the number of points indicated in the top-right-hand corner. Each time you land on your own property, you receive twice the points shown.

Winning Sets: Wise animal (rooster, owl, turtle and lion); toy soldiers (A, B, C and D); one-eyed teddy bears (I, II, III and IV); look fors (answers to questions, love, friendship and good health)

Player One's Properties/Score	Player Two's Properties/Score

Game Card Property Pieces

On this page are the sixteen pieces for *Kenny's Window*. Cut them out and place them on oaktag to prolong their usability. Place a little box next to the gameboard as a storage area. Each time someone lands on an appropriate board space, he receives points and one of the game cards to verify property ownership. It also makes property trading much easier. The next time you play the game, design your own game card property pieces. Design a gameboard and create your own educational board game. Pick a theme. Then try to add important facts and intellectual flavor to your game.

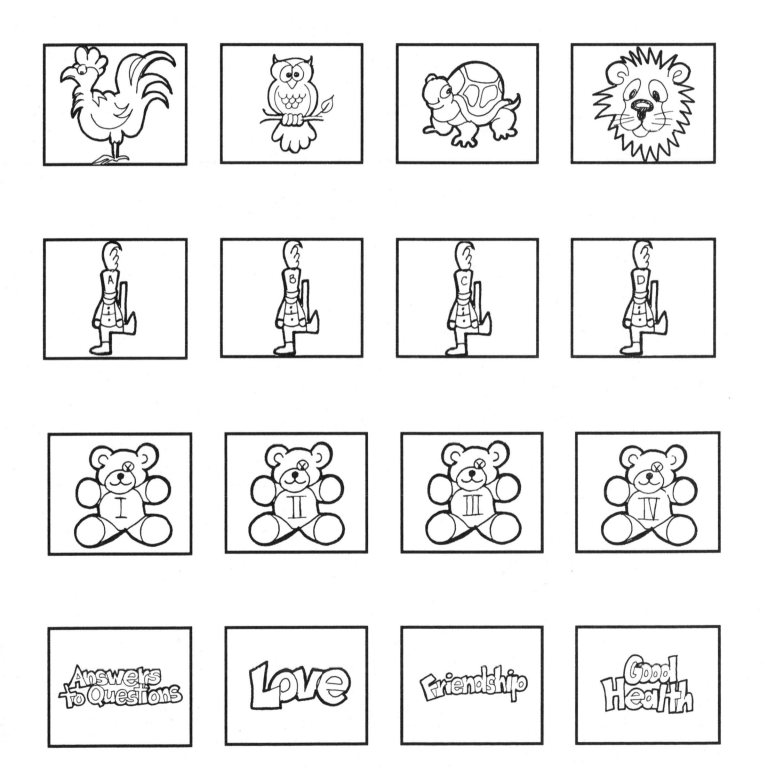

Kenny's Window

3 · 4 · 5 Answers to Questions · 6

2 Pick a Vocabulary Card · 7 Pick a Toss Up Card

1 START · 8

12 · 11 Love · 10 · 9

13 · 20 FINISH

14 · 19

15 Friendship · 16 Pick a Fact Card · 17 · 18 Good Health

Fact Cards

Toss Up Cards

Vocabulary Cards

GA1430

Write Like a Master
Additional Suggestions

The fifty suggestions contained on these pages are good follow-ups to the writing you have completed in each unit of this activity book. You are reminded that a good writer has an excellent vocabulary, can paint various situations and characters and is able to put himself/herself in the shoes of the person he/she is describing in the writing being undertaken. Try to picture yourself in each situation that follows. Experiment with vocabulary words that you haven't used before. Branch off and create new ideas and situations for each challenge below. Try to be a better writer in the situations that "you aren't wild about" than in the ones you say are "really neat ideas" and can't wait to start writing. Recopy each idea into a "master write notebook." That way you can carry them a lot further than the lines that are provided below. Children who have the use of computers may write their stories in a special section on their computer disks. This way their stories can be further expanded or used in future years to support other writing projects that they may be given. Try to stay close to a central theme in each master write, even though creative branch-offs are encouraged.

1. The kids in school call me Plastic Person. For some reason raindrops bounce right off of my skin. I know they bounce off of everyone's skin, but they really fly off of mine. Every rainy day kids are waiting at my door to walk to school with me just to see this happen. No one else in my family _____

    _____

    _____

2. My brother Billy, age 7, is a human dictionary. Every word you ask him, he knows. Sometimes it is fun to have him around, while at others it is a real pain. My mom says he has a photographic memory. That is when_____

    _____.

    She said it all started when _____

    _____

    _____

3. Fresh air! Boy, do I enjoy my two-week vacation here on Earth. You people on Earth take it for granted. Living on Romulac V and breathing man-made oxygen in a giant atmospheric bubble that surrounds each city is like _____

    _____

    _____

    _____

4. Bubble gum! Do you know all the good and bad things that you can do with it? Here are my three favorite good things and three favorite not so good things. I'll try to keep my not so good things in the more tasteful category; get the joke? More tasteful category! They are

    _____

    _____

    _____

GA1430

5. My dog Shelby sleeps with me every night. She's good company and a great watchdog. If it weren't for her fleas, Mom wouldn't mind. Every time I scratch, Mom thinks the dog gave me fleas. You should see it when _____

_____

_____

6. Here is my recipe for "killer cookies," first place winner at our school baking contest. By the way, remember that this is for professional student bakers and should be tried only under parent supervision. Good luck with my recipe. First, you take_____

_____

_____

7. We are lost! What do you mean, how do I know we are lost? After a half an hour of going around in circles, it is easy to tell we are lost. Some other tell-tale signs are _____

_____

_____

8. Did you ever read Patrick Catlings' *Chocolate Touch*? That is the story of the child who turns everything he touches into chocolate. Well, after reading the book, everything that I put in my mouth tastes like chocolate. Should I tell the school librarian to take the book off of the shelf, or should I wait until the next person takes the book out? Then I can ask him if the same thing has happened to him. He'll probably think that I am crazy. Maybe I should just _____

_____

_____

9. Wake up! Wake up! Something very strange is at the front door. No, it is not the milkman. No, it is not the paper boy. Just put your slippers on and look. I'll be hiding in the closet if you need me. Please be _____

_____

_____

10. Let's go fishing. I can't think of a better way to spend the afternoon. Remember the time we went to "green pond"? You were a riot. I never laughed so hard. Why can't we do that again? Bring your _____

_____

_____

11. Hi there, best friend (sneakily smiling). I am going to the dentist today and would like to know if you would trade places with me. I have lots of things that I could trade you if you would do this for me. I could give you my_____

_____

_____

12. Jose Canseco and Kirby Puckett are my two favorite baseball players. I think I like them because of their home run power. I've seen them live because _____

_____

_____

13. Welcome to _____'s (your name) Top Ten Countdown Show brought to you every Friday night at 6:00 p.m. by the makers of _____ (product sponsoring your show). My selections for best records of the month in the country and western, soul, rock and roll, and pop categories are _____

_____

_____

14. Headlining today's news is this interesting story from a little town in Oregon. It seems _____

_____

_____

15. Most scientists say that the caveman could not exist in the time of the dinosaurs. They think that his ideas would be too primitive to survive the giant size and cunning of most of the creatures of the time. I do not believe this to be true, and I am here to outline a plan of survival that I know the caveman would have used if he lived at the same time as the dinosaur. _____

_____

_____

16. The MacKenzie Horse Farm is the most famous horse breeding operation in the United States. Their training methods are quite different from most of the other ranches in the area. However, their success rate shows that different, in this case, really is better. Their methods include _____

_____

_____

17. My deeds as "Marvin the Marvelous" would make Encyclopedia Brown look like a beginner. No, I am not a member of the Worldwide Wrestling Association. The *marvelous* in the middle of my name describes how I am at finding missing pets, lost personal articles and lost persons. I am the one who solved the mystery of _____

_____

_____

18. Go for it! You go for it! Why am I the one that always takes the risks? The last time I went for it I ended up in the hospital with everyone in town laughing at the only person in Switchover Junction with _____

_____

_____

19. This pen keeps writing in reverse. I am moving my hands trying to write a letter to my sister. My mind and my hand said "Hi, Pat," but when I look at what is written it says "Hi, Tap." This is amazing, but what use would anyone have for a pen that writes in reverse? You_____

_____

_____

20. The best way to save money is to _____

_____

_____

21. I have changed my hairstyle three times this month. People say that those people who change their hair that often aren't happy with their lives. I am only ten, so how can I not be happy with my life? I keep changing my hairstyle because _____

_____

_____

22. The Learning Lollipop is a big hit at school. Whatever you are reading while the lollipop is in your mouth can't be forgotten. It is made by the Hershey chocolate company and few people, at first, believed it was true. It was innocently discovered by a female scientist who was _____

_____

_____

23. What do you think the scariest amusement ride is? Is it the Cyclone roller coaster, or is it the "human standup and be turned over while spinning" wheel? Maybe you have a choice of your own? Something more scary and more death defying! Well, now is the time to tell about it, if you dare _____

_____

_____

24. The computer phone is the newest invention that every kid in school wants. It is a cross between the latest computer games and a working telephone. You can program it to _____

_____

_____

25. I'll never be able to use that computer. There is something about me and machines. I have what people call technophobia. It is a fear of anything technical or to do with machines. I am in a club of other technophobics, and the stories they tell are astounding. My three favorites stories about this problem concern _____

_____

_____

26. I just read a story about wing walkers. In the early days of airplanes, because of their slower speeds, people would do all types of crazy stunts on the wings of a flying plane. If you've seen old-time movies, you have an idea of what this is all about. It was very dangerous and a hard way to make a living, but I assumed people did it _____

_____

_____

27. My favorite science fiction writer is Isaac Asimov. He wrote a paper about a substance that dissolves one second before you add water to it. Most people can't explain this idea, but if you think about it, you'll like the creativity. It is definitely possible or is it? Maybe it _____

_____

_____

28. I just designed the inner tube obstacle course to go with the water slide at our local outdoor park. The course has water running at ten miles an hour and five main tasks and three minor ones. The tasks do not have to be completed in order. Each inner tube has a timer that stops when the eight tasks are concluded. Each hour the person with the fastest completion time gets another free ride. The tasks include _____

_____

_____

GA1430

29. The name of my new book is *Why People Can't Resist the Game of Bingo*. It is being published by Simon and Simon of Chicago. It is a book that anyone could have written. It contains lots of insights about people, but it also includes my five steps for winning at bingo. Those steps are _____

_____

_____

30. This is the answering machine of _____ (your name or the name of your company). We are _____

_____

_____

31. Skintastic is the greatest invention of the twenty-first century. It has doubled the world's food sources and has, probably, sustained the lives of millions of people. When rubbed on the nonedible parts of meats, fruits and vegetables (for example, banana skins, bones, nutshells, pits), it makes them edible. This has increased the world's edible foods by over 30 percent. It is expensive, but when weighed against the normal grocery bill, it is a real money saver. It is _____

_____

_____

32. Jennifer Jump Rope, that's me, the school champ. I can do any rhyme and turn and jump on a dime. You know what I mean, if you have ever been in a school yard at recess. It _____

_____

_____

33. Every school in America has a show-and-tell period for kids in the lower grades. My favorite show-and-tell items when I was smaller were _____

_____. If I could bring in three things now, they would be

_____

_____

34. My schoolbag has more compartments than a hundred-passenger train. There are compartments for _____

I think it should have compartments for _____

_____

35. My brother is called "Mister TV" by all the kids in the neighborhood. He has been this way since he was four years old. It surely doesn't take a genius to guess why everyone calls him this. Just look at him or talk to him and _____

_____

_____

36. I just don't fit into today's world. I think I would better fit in during the time of Robin Hood and his merry men. I'd have to live off of my wits and survival skills. My love of the outdoors would _____

_____

_____

37. If I could build a best girlfriend and best boyfriend, I would make sure that they had the following characteristics and personality traits _____

_____

_____

38. Everyone talks about making school a better place, but no one really does anything about it. If I were in charge of designing three things that would make school better, the three would most certainly include _____

_____

_____

39. I am so terrible at mathematics that I almost wish there were a world without numbers that would make me an honorary citizen. It isn't that hard to imagine, and I bet that hundreds of kids would join me there. Anytime numbers were involved, you would just _____

_____

_____

40. Why do you think sleep was invented? It stops you from doing so many things. A large portion of our productive lives is wasted sleeping. If you didn't have to sleep, the world would _____

_____

_____

41. It seems like we have been on this train forever. Someone has to think of something to do while riding on a train after the usual playing cards, reading, watching TV and sleeping. How about if I design a new and revolutionary type of train travel? It would make travel by plane, car or bus obsolete. My super train would have _____

_____

_____

42. Not one more vegetable! My body is turning green from all the vegetables you have been giving me. Do me a favor and add yogurt to the "not one more" list. What happened to all the great foods we used to eat like_____

_____

_____

43. It is always the things that you would like to forget that you keep thinking about. I think that is because too many people concentrate on the negative rather than the positive. Everyone's life has 50 percent good things in it and 50 percent bad things in it. I guess you can drive yourself crazy just thinking of the bad. If I could only get the thoughts of_____

_____

_____ out of my mind.

44. My favorite TV show would combine the characters and ideas from my three favorite movies. I know this might sound weird, but the movies I would combine to make a TV show are _____

_____

The show would be one that the whole family could enjoy. Each part of it would have something for each age group in a typical household. For Mom and Dad there would be

_____

_____

45. There are only five drinks that children are allowed to have: milk, soda, juice, water and tea. Most kids are bored with these drinks. That's why Liquidall can't miss at becoming the most popular drink of our time. Just think, where else can you find a drink that has so many exciting properties and is good for you at the same time? It _____

_____

_____

46. The Teddy Bear should be named Pennsylvania's (please feel free to place the name of your state in this location) state doll. There can't be any other more meaningful toy. Everyone has had one, and I can't think of another toy that would be more acceptable unless you think of the _____

_____

_____

47. My antipollution campaign is changing the appearance of our town, thanks to the cooperation of our schools, businesses and local civic groups. The reason my campaign is different from those that have come before it is that its features are rewarding and easy to follow. Its key points are _____

_____

_____

48. The People Light is an energy saver and people pleaser everywhere it is used. Each People Light bulb has a special sensor that adjusts the light to the brightness preference of the person using that particular room. For instance, I like a room super bright because of my bad eyesight, while Grandma likes it half as bright. When I use a room, the light brightens. When Grandma uses a room, the light comes on dimmer. If both of us were in the room at the same time, it would average the light that we need or adjust the one closest to us. This same type of sensor could be used for other things also like the _____

_____

_____

49. The fiercest and most studied sea creature is the great white shark. Every class I take, they say the same thing. Why don't they talk about the salmon with the same reverence as the great white? (Substitute your favorite fish) is far superior in intelligence, spawning and survival techniques. From Russia to the United States, it is known as a great fighting and eating fish. Who would want to eat the great white shark? Why can't oceanographers _____

_____

_____

50. I don't know why I buy packs of baseball, football, hockey and basketball cards. All my friends make these great finds, and I get just about nothing out of what I open. You would think that in fifteen cards something would appear. This is the last pack that I will ever open. Here goes! Impossible! I finally did it! The most-sought-after card of my generation! So what if I am exaggerating! I no longer consider myself a loser. Here is the card that has brought new meaning to pack opening. A _____

_____

_____

Ideas and Illustrations Supplement
Bulletin Boards

Dear cartographers, architects, sign painters, teachers, students, and bulletin board makers of America,

There are nine pages in this section. Each page represents a month of the school year. The page is divided into two parts. The upper section contains an idea for a classroom or hall bulletin board for the particular month indicated. Teachers might want to take a piece of transparency paper, trace the bulletin board idea, put it on an overhead projector, and outline the enlarged image the projector creates. The lower section is a bulletin board that has been started but needs student help to complete. Students are asked to give their input as to the direction additional writing and illustration should take. Please complete the student bulletin board with your original and humorous ideas. A monthly clothesline of student bulletin boards makes a great display. A blank bulletin board has been provided below for students who would like to create a bulletin board from scratch. Students can use this blank board to create ideas for their other subjects as well. Transfer your best ideas to 11" x 14" (27.94 x 35.56 cm) art paper and pin the class' best work up in the hallway. Try having a bulletin board contest after your teacher gives you a general theme for your original work.

Student name _____

My bulletin board theme is _____

Bulletin Board Idea for September

September's Top Tunes

Student-Developed Bulletin Board for September

September's Signs of a Good Education

Bulletin Board Idea for October
Camp Out with a Good Book

Student-Developed Bulletin Board for October
The Book Wizard's October Suggestions

Bulletin Board Idea for November

Let Your Mind Be a Vocabulary Volcano

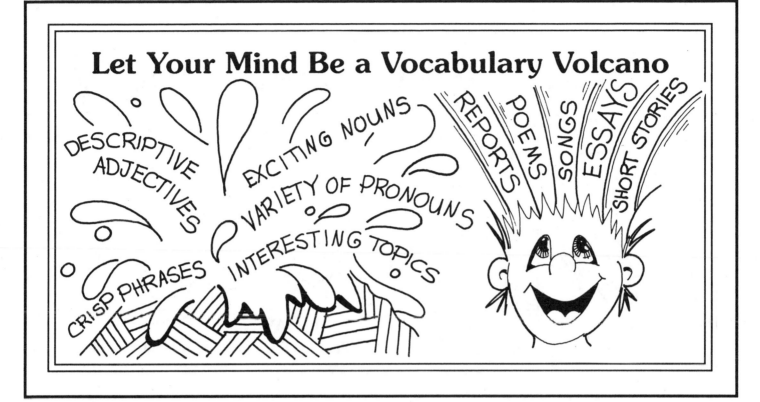

Let Your Mind Be a Vocabulary Volcano

DESCRIPTIVE ADJECTIVES

EXCITING NOUNS

VARIETY OF PRONOUNS

CRISP PHRASES

INTERESTING TOPICS

REPORTS

POEMS

SONGS

ESSAYS

SHORT STORIES

Student-Developed Bulletin Board for November

Eight Favorite Turkey Talk Subjects

Eight Favorite Turkey Talk Subjects

TAKE A PEEK AT MY EIGHT FAVORITE TOPICS TO GOBBLE (DISCUSS).

1.	ANIMAL CARE / FEEDING
2.	
3	
4.	WHAT MAKES A GOOD FRIEND
5.	
6.	
7.	ENDANGERED SPECIES
8.	

GA1430

Bulletin Board Idea for December

December's Delights

Student-Developed Bulletin Board for December

Dance Steps for December

Bulletin Board Idea for January

A Penny for Your Thoughts On

Student-Developed Bulletin Board for January

Working on January Ideas

Bulletin Board Idea for February

Heart-Stopping Books and Stories

Heart-Stopping Books and Stories

Student-Developed Bulletin Board for February

The Groundhog Was Too Busy Reading to See His Shadow

The Groundhog Was Too Busy Reading to See His Shadow

GA1430

Bulletin Board Idea for March

March Up to Great Authors

Student-Developed Bulletin Board for March

Drumming Up Myths and Legends

Bulletin Board Idea for April

April's Flower Power Brings Your Mental Garden to Life

April's Flower Power Brings Your Mental Garden to Life

BOTANY

GEOLOGY

CHEMISTRY

BIOLOGY

ASTRONOMY

METEOROLOGY

Student-Developed Bulletin Board for April

Spring Out of Your Educational Rut

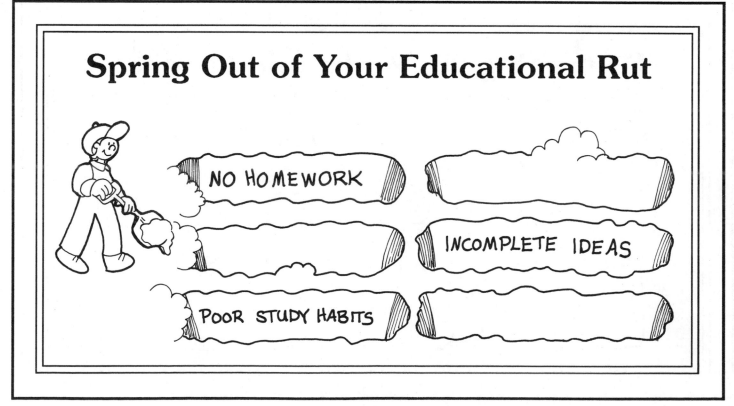

Spring Out of Your Educational Rut

NO HOMEWORK

INCOMPLETE IDEAS

POOR STUDY HABITS

Bulletin Board Idea for May

Memories of May

Memories of May

MUSEUM TRIP

GREAT GRADES

CLASS DANCE

FROG JUMPING CONTEST

NEW LITERARY ADVENTURES

OUTDOOR SPORTS

Student-Developed Bulletin Board for May

Make May Meaningful

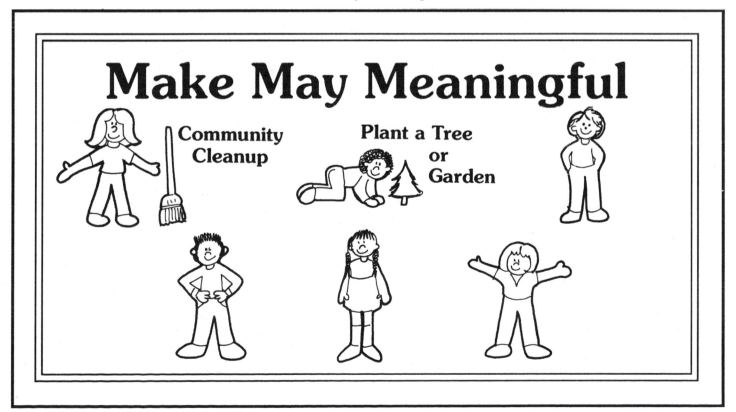

Make May Meaningful

Community Cleanup

Plant a Tree or Garden

On your own, try to create two bulletin boards for June, July and August.

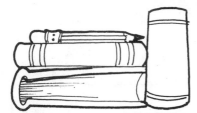

Short-Term Projects
Additional Ideas
Student Project Thinking Sheets

One of the greatest challenges in teaching in a resource type program is the development of creative, challenging and educationally enriching short-term projects that students and their families can work on before being presented in the classroom. Each week I see ninety-five students from kindergarten to the eighth grade class level. Their projects have to have reading, literature, mathematics, social studies and science integrated into them. Some children I see for as long as five years. This totals over two hundred different projects. I have self-choice days where each child selects his own homework. We also take student suggestions on topics that follow our standard curriculum. I can't do anything the regular classroom teacher does, so this puts me further in a "project-idea-producing" corner. I require that each project must have some type of picture, prop and writing to support it. Projects are never just handed in. They must be presented to the whole class. The following pages contain additional ideas. Each idea is followed by a thinking sheet. The next pages will help the students organize their ideas and resources. After completing each sheet, they will find getting started on their projects is much easier. Students will be asked the following:

What is your name? _____

What is the name of your project? _____

List the theme of the picture you are going to draw to support your project. _____

_____

Brief picture description: _____

_____

What props and three-dimensional figures are you going to use with your presentation? _____

_____

Will you be using any charts or graphs to present your ideas? How? _____

_____

Will any of your classmates assist you in your presentation? What will their jobs be? _____

_____

Write the first fifteen lines of your opening remarks on the back of this planning sheet.

What is the most creative part of your _____ (project's name) project production? Why and how is this different from other people's ideas on the same subject? _____

_____

Pirate Creativity
Short-Term Project I
Theme Sheet

1. **Pirate Patch Day**. You are a pirate who, because of an injury in a sword fight, must wear a protective eye patch. Since you want to be known as the most creative pirate on the high seas, you have to design an eye patch for each day of the week. Three of these patches must show your love of knowledge. You can do this by featuring books, movies, school subjects, or worthwhile causes on your eye patches. Instead of a patch for each day, you might want to design a patch for seven special occasions–football game, school dance, wedding, birth of brother or sister, new dog.

What is your name? _____

What is the name of your project? _____

List the theme of the picture you are going to draw to support your project. _____

_____

Brief picture description: _____

_____

What props and three-dimensional figures are you going to use with your presentation? _____

_____

_____

Will you be using any charts or graphs to present your ideas? How? _____

_____

Will any of your classmates assist you in your presentation? What will their jobs be? _____

_____

Write the first fifteen lines of your opening remarks on the back of this planning sheet.

What is the most creative part of your pirate project production? How and why is this so different from other people's ideas? _____

_____

GA1430

Pirate Creativity
Short-Term Project I
Eye Patch Blank Master

Use colored pencils to create seven distinctive ideas for a creative pirate's eye patch.

Example: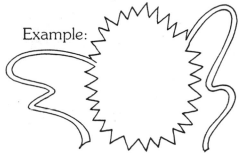

Number your patches from 1 to 7, with 1 being your most creative work and 7 your least creative.

GA1430

Creativity with Monsters, Myths and Legends
Short-Term Project II
Theme Sheet

2. **Cyclops Eyeball Day.** After studying the parts of the eye and being introduced to the Cyclops in our myths and legends text, each child must bring in a creative eyeball. My favorite was a student who made a giant papier-mâché eyeball that blinked to show a giant Cyclops standing in the middle of it. In your presentation you must show a knowledge of the parts of the eye and the myths you have read.

What is your name? _____

What is the name of your project? _____

List the theme of the picture you are going to draw to support your project. _____

_____

What eyeball parts will appear in your production? _____

_____

Whose eyeball are you re-creating?_____

Brief picture description: _____

_____

What props and three-dimensional figures are you going to use with your presentation? _____

_____

Will you be using any charts or graphs to present your ideas? How? _____ _____

_____

Will any of your classmates assist you in your presentation? What will their jobs be? _____

_____

Write the first fifteen lines of your opening remarks on the back of this planning sheet.

What is the most creative part of your eyeball project production? How and why is this so different from other people's ideas? _____

_____

Draw a picture below and hand it in before you present your project.

GA1430

Creativity with Monsters, Myths and Legends
Short-Term Project II
Eyeball Blank Master

Design the Cyclops' outfit; then label the scientific parts of each eyeball.

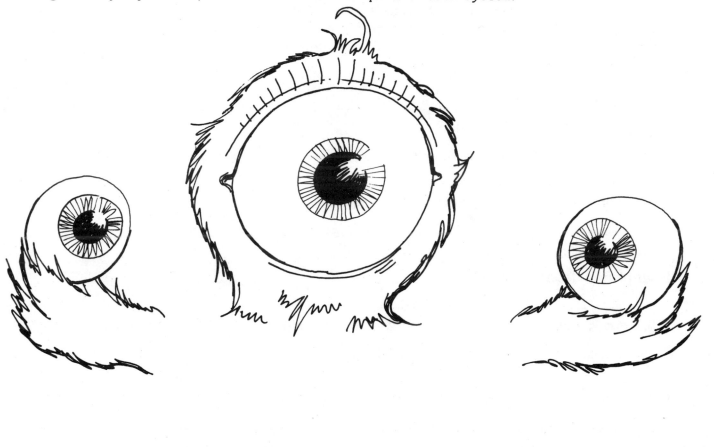

List the basic parts of an eyeball below. Then use a humorous approach to label ten parts of the Cyclops.

GA1430

Creativity with Award-Winning Books
Short-Term Project III
Theme Sheet

3. **Caldecott/Newbery Walking Advertisement Day.** Like most teachers, after studying the Newbery and Caldecott award winners and honor books, I had each student come in as his favorite award book. He/She has to talk to the class as the book, not as a person who just read the book. Students wanted to repeat this the next week with a different book. Instead, the idea of people who carried billboards (slabs of wood in front of their chests and over their backs) over their bodies was introduced to the class. The next week they were walking billboards with a Newbery book on the front and a Caldecott book on the back. We, of course, paraded through and presented to all the classrooms on our floor. I don't recommend this for everyone, but if there were book tattoos (washable, of course) that must be worn while reading your best-loved book, what would your seven best tattoos look like?

What is your name? _____

What is the name of your project? _____

List the theme of the picture you are going to draw to support your project. _____

_____

What attracted you to the two books you are going to feature on your body billboards? _____

_____

_____

What is the appeal of a tattoo? _____

Brief picture description: _____

_____

What props and three-dimensional figures are you going to use with your presentation? _____

_____

_____

Will you be using any charts or graphs to present your ideas? How? _____

_____

Will any of your classmates assist you in your presentation? What will their jobs be? _____

_____

Write the first fifteen lines of your opening remarks on the back of this planning sheet.

What is the idea that is most special on your billboard? _____

Draw a picture below and hand it in before you present your project.

GA1430

Creativity with Award-Winning Books
Short-Term Project III
Student Billboards

Two girls and two boys are holding their award-winning billboards. Complete your four best award-worthy designs on each child's masterpiece.

GA1430

A City Named After Me
Short-Term Project IV
Theme Sheet

4. **Palumboville or Susan City Day.** You have a city named after you. Bring in the blueprint for your city, a model (no Legos/Tinker Toys) and a descriptive tour of your city. Like the Kennedy, Johnson or Rockefeller library, please highlight the town's library. We did this activity on returning from the Philadelphia Fire Museum. Since Philadelphia was one of the first cities to have a fire department, the class's models featured their creative firehouse instead of a library.

What is your city's name?_____

What is the name of your project? _____

List the theme of the picture you are going to draw to support your project. _____

_____

Brief picture description: _____

_____

If I were a new visitor to your city, what three things would make me want to come back or live there? _____

_____

What props and three-dimensional figures are you going to use with your presentation? _____

_____

Will you be using any charts or graphs to present your ideas? How? _____

_____

Will any of your classmates assist you in your presentation? What will their jobs be? _____

_____

Write the first fifteen lines of your opening remarks on the back of this planning sheet.

What is the most creative part of your newly developed city project production? How and why is this so different from other people's ideas? _____

Draw a picture below and hand it in before you present your project.

153

City Named After Me
Short-Term Project IV
Theme Sheet

You will find half of a church, firehouse, library, skyscraper and amusement ride below. Each of these things could be in your model city. Complete each drawing in the style you have in mind for your city.

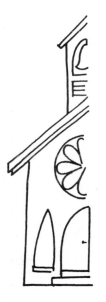

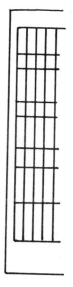

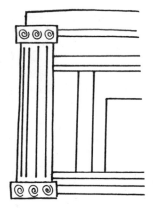

GA1430

Take Me Out to Baseball History
Short-Term Project V
Theme Sheet

5. **Historical Baseball Card Day.** Design three baseball cards that have a split design. One half of the card shows a famous event in baseball like Babe Ruth hitting sixty home runs in 1927. The second half of the card must show an historical event that happened the same year. The first solo flight across the Atlantic by Charles Lindbergh in the *Spirit of St. Louis* was completed in 1927, also.

What is the name of your favorite ball player? _____

_____

What is the name of your project? _____

List the theme of the picture you are going to draw to support your project. _____

_____

Brief picture description: _____

You are a sport's nut. You could live in any city. Compare all the sports teams in the major cities. In which city would you choose to live? On another sheet of paper write a mini analysis of each team. Be sure you are not a "hometown" team rooter.

Pick five major cities and list their best tourist attractions. See if you can research which of your cities attracts the greatest number of tourists.

What props and three-dimensional figures are you going to use with your presentation? Can you give your cards a 3-D or hologram look? _____

_____

Will you be using any charts or graphs to present your ideas? How? _____

_____

What kind of sport statistics will you be using on the back of your cards?_____

Will any of your classmates assist you in your presentation? What will their jobs be? _____

_____

Did you think about taking your own picture and mounting it on a card? Who would you claim to be? _____

_____

Write the first fifteen lines of your opening remarks on the back of this planning sheet.

What is the most creative part of your historical baseball project production? How and why is this so different from other people's ideas? _____

Draw a picture below and hand it in before you present your project.

Take Me Out to Baseball History
Short-Term Project V
Card Greats

Baseball cards that have split themes generally come in four different designs. Please remember to spend as much time designing the historical side of each card as you do the side with sports information.

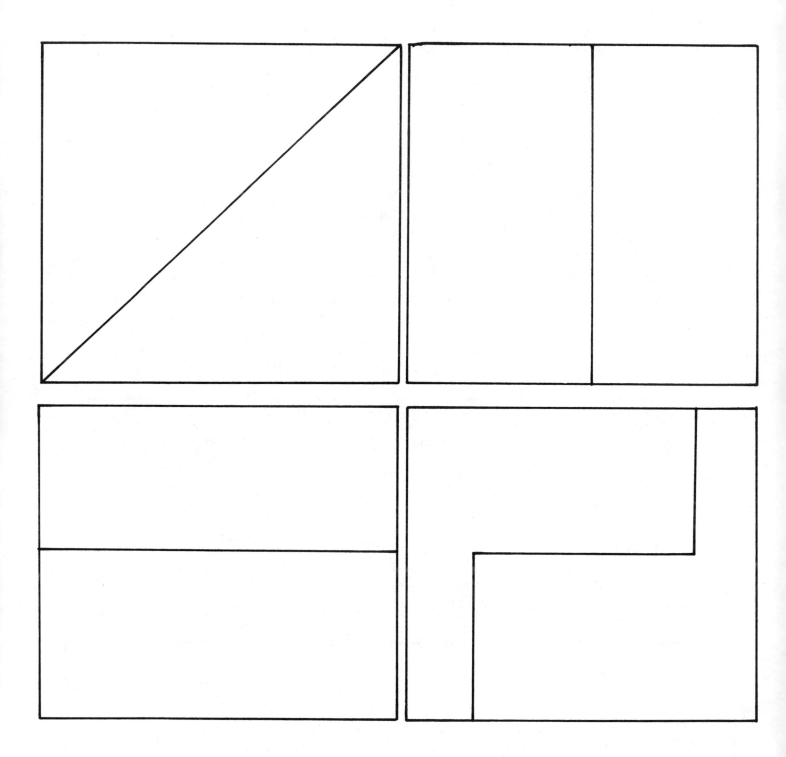

"Egg"citing Ideas
Short-Term Project VI
Theme Sheet

6. **Adopt an Egg Day.** Many schools do the activity where uncooked eggs must be put in some type of student-designed protective container before being dropped from the roof of the school building. Hopefully, the egg will survive the fall and not crack. Added to this activity is that each child must keep the egg with him twenty-four hours a day for a week and present in diary form four of the memorable happenings of the week. Upper grade classes do this to show children how difficult caring for a young child twenty-four hours a day is. One of my students told the story of not wanting to take the egg out with her, so she had to get an egg baby-sitter. "Do you know how hard it is to find an egg baby-sitter in the phone book," she relayed to us. "You just can't trust your egg to anyone."

What is your egg's name? _____

What is the name of your project? _____

List the theme of the picture you are going to draw to support your project. _____

_____

Brief picture description: _____

_____

Do you think of eggs as an eating enjoyment? _____

_____

What props and three-dimensional figures are you going to use with your presentation? _____

_____

Will you be using any charts or graphs to present your ideas? How? _____

_____

Will a parachute or classmate assist you in your presentation? What will their jobs be? _____

_____

Before dropping your egg, record your amazing, indestructible egg speech on the back of this planning sheet.

What is the most creative part of your egg project production? How and why is this so different from other people's ideas? _____

Draw a picture of the egg drop event in the area below. Show your expected outcome in your drawing.

"Egg"citing Ideas
Short-Term Project VI
Egg Resumé

Draw a picture of the way your egg looked at birth, school age and old age.

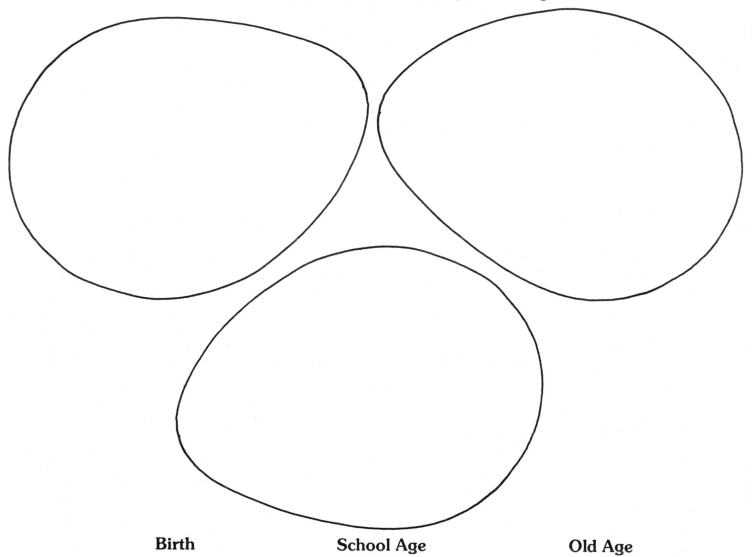

Birth   **School Age**   **Old Age**

Fill in the following vital statistics before your egg is dropped in your protective container.

Date of birth _____

Place of birth _____

Parents' names _____

_____

Height standing on end _____

Measurement around middle _____

Weight _____

Measurement around lengthwise _____

Outstanding feature _____

Best memory _____

_____

School attended _____

If married, explain. _____

_____

GA1430

About Face Creativity
Short-Term Project VII
Theme Sheet

7. **Two-Face Day.** This activity was used as part of our writing dialogue follow-up. The idea was taken from a television show which featured a character who had a two-sided face, and each side represented a different personality. Students were to design two masks or a face and a mask. The two characters represented were to have a discussion with each other. A second grader did Snow White talking to Grumpy.

What are your two names? _____ _____

How are your two characters different?_____

_____

List the theme of the picture you are going to draw to support your project. _____

Brief picture description: _____

_____

What props and three-dimensional figures are you going to use with your presentation? _____

_____

Will you be using any masks or face paintings to present your ideas? How? _____

_____

Will any of your classmates assist you in your presentation? How about twins talking to twins?

_____

Write the first fifteen lines of your opening remarks on the back of this planning sheet.

What is the most creative part of your face project production? How and why is this so different from other people's ideas? _____

Draw a picture below and hand it in before you present your project. Place four ideas you could have used for your faces but didn't on another piece of paper.

GA1430

About Face Creativity
Short-Term Project VII
Face to Face

Before doing this work sheet you should find five challenging faces you would like to draw. Cut each face in half. Glue or staple one of the halves to a piece of construction paper. Draw the missing half.

Now design the two faces below in the one head. Place your best drawing on a classroom clothesline.

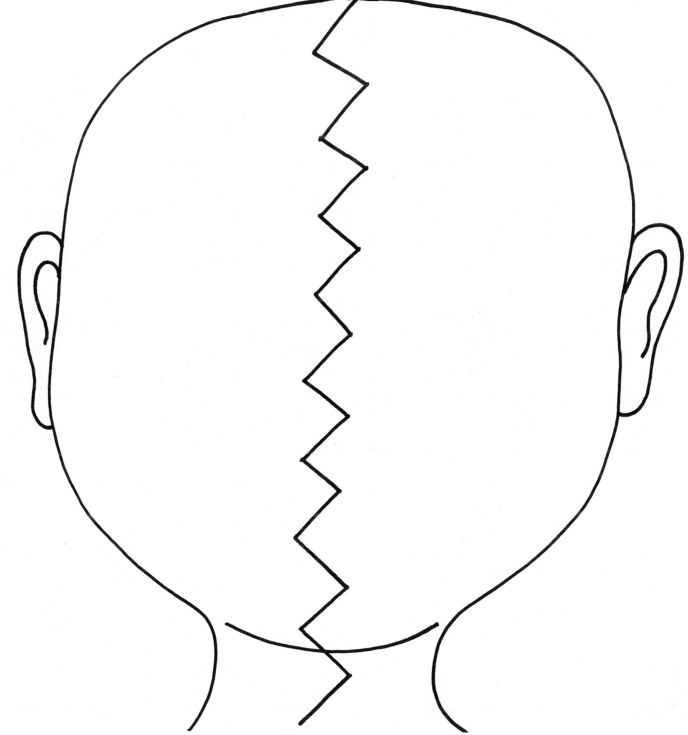

160

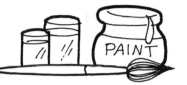

Great American Painters
Short-Term Project VIII
Face to Face

8. **Henry Ossawa Tanner Day.** Henry Tanner's seascapes, animal studies, southern depictions, and religious paintings are an ideal start for memory presentations. We took ten of his best pictures and put them in a slide presentation. Each student had to study each slide's background and write an introduction and description of the slide. Paintings like *Lion Licking Paw* are excellent for the lower grades, while *The Banjo Lesson* is excellent for upper grade students. This can be done with any artist and helps train students in giving professional presentations. Tanner has Philadelphia roots, and his wide variety of topics while trying to find his place/acceptance in the art world gives every child something to choose from and an understanding of what a creative person has to go through to express himself.

What is the name of your favorite painter? _____

_____

Explain why you think this painter would be good drawing illustrations in children's books. ___

_____

What is the name of your project? _____

List the theme of the picture you are going to draw to support your project. _____

_____

Brief picture description: _____

_____

What props and three-dimensional figures are you going to use with your presentation? _____

_____

Will you be using any charts or graphs to present your ideas? How? _____

_____

After examining Tanner's paintings, why do you think he was selected to get children of all

ages interested in describing art? _____

_____

Write the first fifteen lines of your opening remarks on the back of this planning sheet.
What is the most creative part of your art project production and speech? How and why is this so different from other people's ideas? Try having three different characters (you) describing the picture that you chose. _____

_____

Draw a picture on another sheet of paper and hand it in before you present your project.

                                                                                    GA1430

Great American Painter's
Short-Term Project VIII
Tanner's Topics

Tanner's four areas of expertise are framed for you below. Each one has been started. See if you can finish each painting in the same style Tanner used.

| Seascape | Southern Life |
| Religious | Animal |

GA1430

A Store Owner's Delight
Short-Term Project IX
Theme Sheet

9. **Blue Store and Crazy Tie Day.** Each child is the owner of a store that sells only blue things. The color is optional. Lower grades sell things that start with a particular letter. You are also known for the crazy ties that you wear. You are to design your store front and present your three best blue products. Your tie design must be coordinated to the product you are presenting. Try designing a tie for your three favorite holidays. How about a tie that people wear to remind them of their pets or children?

What is your tie or color store called? _____

Do you think color attracts people to an item more than anything else? If so, did you base your color selection on the color that most people would select in a preference test? _____

_____

What is the name of your project? _____

List the theme of the picture you are going to draw to support your project. _____

_____

Brief picture description: _____

What props and three-dimensional figures are you going to use with your presentation? How about five dolls each wearing one of your tie creations? _____

_____

Will you be using any charts or graphs to present your ideas? How? _____

_____

Make a chart showing your weekly or monthly store or tie sales.

Which of your classmates would look best in your ties? Do your ties come in men's and women's styles? _____

_____

Write the first fifteen lines of your opening remarks on the back of this planning sheet.

What is the most creative part of your store project productions? How and why is this so different from other people's ideas? _____

Draw a picture below and hand it in before you present your project.

163

A Store Owner's Delight
Short-Term Project IX
Tie Mania

Six giant ties are outlined below. Place your best ideas for designs on them. One, two and three can be designed using crayon or pencil. Tie four has to be a collage of people's faces; tie five cutouts of cars; tie six cutout words.

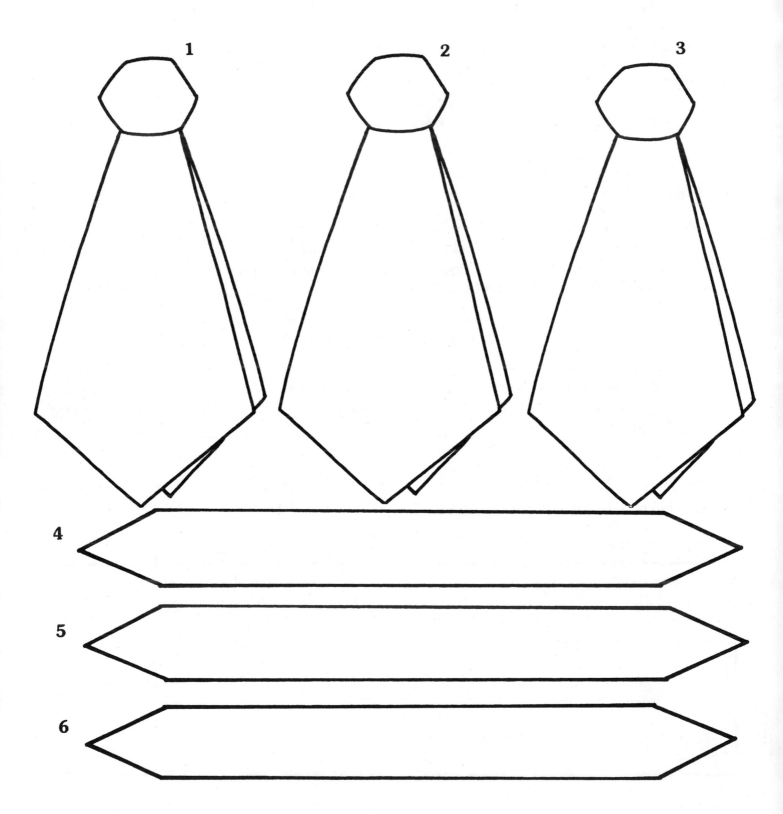

GA1430

The Teddy Bears' Picnic
Short-Term Project X
Face to Face

10. The Philadelphia zoo's largest attended promotion is called **Teddy Bear Day**. Teddy Bear Day in the classroom requires everyone to bring in his teddy bear and select an animal from literature that is the teddy bear's best friend. After the literature presentations of the teddy bears and their book friends, mathematics takes over. You can collect all sorts of teddy bear data; then chart and graph the results. Some suggestions would be teddy bear weight, height, arm span, chest size, foot size, age, distance school is from place of purchase or where you received the teddy bear as a gift, or ranking the most outrageous teddy bear tall tale story.

What is your teddy bear's name? _____

Who is the teddy bear's companion? _____

What is the name of your project? _____

Why do you think teddy bears are so important to young children? _____

_____

The Velveteen Rabbit is an excellent story. Do you think it would be just as good if a teddy

bear came to life? _____

_____

List the theme of the picture you are going to draw to support your project. _____

_____

Brief picture description: _____

_____

What props and three-dimensional figures are you going to use with your presentation? ___

_____

Will you be using any charts or graphs to present your ideas? How? _____

_____

Will any of your classmates assist you in your presentation? What will their jobs be? _____

_____

Write the first fifteen lines of your opening remarks on the back of this planning sheet.

What is the most creative part of your teddy bear project production? How and why is this

so different from other people's ideas? _____

Draw a picture on another sheet of paper and hand it in before you present your project.

GA1430

The Teddy Bears' Picnic
Short-Term Project X
Bear Stomachs

Before designing the four bear stomachs below, look at the designs used on the Care Bears. Try to use a new idea, yet one children will enjoy.

166

A Myriad of Creative Days
Short-Term Project XI
Theme Sheet

11. **Coat Hanger Day**. This is where each child has to dress up a coat hanger as his favorite character from literature or his favorite singer. Some suggestions might be musical hangers, Disney Ride Day where the students design rides for a new theme park that was being built in our town, Television Day where book reports are presented as part of television programs, or Weather Person Day which concerns your first interview for a local station's weather reporter position. You must develop a one-minute presentation that includes maps and weather symbols or X Day where you are upset that the letter X is not used enough in the English language, art or science. Your five suggestions for improving the acceptance of the letter X and X fan club accessories should be a part of your presentation or Miniature Umbrella Day where you list three kinds of umbrellas and the ideal times they should be used. Reverse World Day involves living in a world where everything is reversed. Your parents tell you not to eat your vegetables, and you have to turn on lights when leaving the room. How about Mickey Mouse and Donald Duck Day where these two characters become part of your favorite book. Holiday Day has everyone dressing up as his favorite holiday and presenting a book that would blend in with that holiday's theme. Last, but not least, is Beach Blanket Day where you bring your beach blanket, design two beach towels, one of which salutes your favorite book, and lip-sync your favorite beach tune.

Take your favorite selection from those above and complete the project using the information sheet below.

Rank the three projects that you would like to do.

1. _____

2. _____

3. _____

Why did the first selection appeal to you?_____

_____

List the theme of the picture you are going to draw to support your project selection. _____

_____

Brief picture description: _____

_____

What props and three-dimensional figures are you going to use with your presentation? ____

_____

Will you be using any charts or graphs to present your ideas? How? _____

_____

Will any of your classmates assist you in your presentation? What will their jobs be?_____
_____

Write the first fifteen lines of your opening remarks on the back of this planning sheet.

What is the most creative part of your _____ project production? How and why is this so different from other people's ideas?_____

What idea do you have for a project of your own? _____
_____

Draw a picture below and hand it in before you present your project.

GA1430

Answer Key

Just the Facts, page 3
1. olden times, picture of papa's ship
2. to sea
3. a garden
4. wonderhorn
5. two
6. for goblin's bride
7. ice baby
8. dripped, stared
9. yellow rain cloak
10. forward through the window
11. robber's cave
12. rain
13. a hill
14. letters
15. in an eggshell
16. a stream, water
17. a jig
18. wedding
19. babies
20. hubbub

Drills for Skills, page 6
1. Oreo, rodeo
2. area
3. oleo
4. aura, Laura
5. asea
6. aria
7. aide, aside
8. Asia
9. beau, beaut
10. epee, peeve
11. aloe
12. Erie, eerie
13. ooze, booze
14. ease, easel
15. alee, leave
16. lieu
17. idea, ideal

Just the Facts, page 17
1. thump, dump, clump, lump, bump
2. 1970, for Sadie and Philip
3. his clothes
4. the moon, his mother and father
5. dawn
6. Abbott and Costello
7. Mickey cake
8. milk
9. airplane, to escape
10. to fill it with milk
11. Milky Way
12. in the milk bottle
13. the slide

Just the Facts, page 31
1. a forest
2. hanger, blanket
3. mischief
4. Wild Thing
5. his mother
6. dinner
7. boat
8. over a year
9. teeth
10. rolled
11. be still
12. staring
13. king
14. a rumpus
15. loneliness
16. eat
17. They loved him.
18. vines
19. supper
20. hot
21. white

Vexing Vocabulary, page 49
1. alligator
2. swan
3. turkey
4. sparrow
5. cobra
6. elephant
7. lion
8. robin
9. weevil
10. parrot
11. aardvark
12. swallow
13. chicken
14. boar
15. hippopotamus
16. bear
17. panther

Facts and Opinions, page 50
1. stone's throw
2. their father
3. clasping hands
4. wretch
5. quail, partridge, pheasant
6. larks, linnets
7. the bowmen
8. cut down castle's trees
9. Pebbiaw's land
10. both were

Facts and Opinions, page 51
1. globe thistle
2. north, south, east, west
3. five
4. peace, strength
5. alien, foreign
6. Great Creator
7. weapons
8. underground waters
9. uprooted
10. Mohawk, Oneida, Onondaga, Cayuga and Seneca

Facts and Opinions, page 52
1. squeezed dry
2. empty Bering Sea
3. Gambell
4. the elders
5. whales
6. eight months
7. war
8. the International Date Line
9. Friendship Flight One
10. throughout the world

Drills for Skills I, page 53
1. blossom/bloom
2. well/we
3. apple/ale
4. Zorro/zoo
5. mellow/meow
6. battles/bales
7. hiss/hi
8. Aaron/Ron
9. pretty/prey
10. daddy/day
11. princess/prince
12. summit/suit
13. fluff/flu
14. tosses/toes
15. saddle/sale
16. rally/ray
17. occur/our

Drills for Skills III, page 55
1. done, 1/4
2. lonely, 3/6 = 1/2
3. drone, 2/5
4. stone, 2/5
5. phone, 2/5
6. bone, 1/4
7. Boone, 2/5
8. gone, 1/4
9. honey, 2/5
10. honest, 3/6 = 1/2
11. tone, 1/4
12. clone, 2/5
13. prone, 2/5

Just the Facts, page 68
1. downstairs lion
2. gold
3. out the window
4. yonder
5. the dog ate it
6. pig
8. first night
9. salami
10. a cat
11. six
12. Jennie
13. eat, yum, grow, bite, shout
14. hidden
15. ash tree
16. colored lanterns
17. two
18. letter

Drills for Skills, page 72
1. alarm, 3/5
2. chair, 4/5
3. ship, 3/4
4. flip, 3/4
5. richest, 5/7
6. kneel, 4/5
7. early, 3/5
8. brown, 4/5
9. ribbon, 3/6 = 1/2
10. ahead, 4/5
11. asking, 4/6 = 2/3
12. palmer, 4/6 = 2/3
13. hearth, 5/6
14. headstone, 4/9
15. scratching, 4/10 = 2/5
16. potatoes, 4/8 = 1/2
17. sliver, 5/6

Just the Facts, page 82
1. no
2. six o'clock
3. the lion
4. off to bed
5. lovely
6. moral
7. in bed
8. the lion
9. shook him up and down
10. syrup
11. his head
12. in Pierre's eyes
13. hungry
14. home
15. three
16. care
17. lesson
18. a weekend
19. He laughed.
20. doctor
21. dreadful

169

GA1430

Drills for Skills I, page 85
1. spear
2. scrapple
3. Caribbean
4. jellyfish
5. doughnut
6. corner
7. hammer
8. price
9. beetle
10. clamp
11. plumber
12. sleek

Drills for Skills II, page 86
1. break
2. clear
3. dread
4. early
5. float
6. great
7. happy
8. inner
9. jelly
10. kneel
11. loved
12. moved
13. north
14. ocean
15. plant
16. queen
17. ready
18. smart
19. tough
20. untie
21. video
22. witch
23. X rays
24. young
25. zesty

Just the Facts, page 101
1. rosebud
2. stars
3. cannon fire, smoke, shouts/tumult
4. cake
5. screamed
6. white dove
7. thorns
8. water, roots, cake
9. straw, bed
10. eyes
11. flower
12. wild beasts
13. sun's rays
14. strange, unfamiliar
15. in the bed

Mil **Words**, page 104
1. million
2. mile
3. military
4. smile
5. Millie
6. mild
7. milk
8. mildew
9. mill
10. Milky Way
11. milestone
12. millipede
13. millisecond
14. Milwaukee
15. milliner
16. Milton, John
17. milkweed

Just the Facts, page 115
1. a wish
2. caboose
3. Bucky
4. scare
5. new
6. Switzerland
7. glass
8. chocolate candy bar
9. crying
10. elephant
11. pink, yellow, blue
12. pajama pocket
13. lead soldiers
14. Bucky
15. waterfall, snowy mountains, cowbells
16. a telegram
17. checkerboard
18. finger
19. for a friend
20. pride

Alphabetical I.Q. page 118
1. answer
2. butter
3. closed
4. doctor
5. effect
6. friend
7. greedy
8. height
9. inside
10. joyous
11. killed
12. lovely
13. middle
14. notice
15. outlaw
16. pardon
17. quiets, quells
18. remove
19. starve
20. target
21. upends
22. verify
23. wisdom
24 x-rayed
25. yelled
26. zipper

GA1430